Today's Hospital

Today's Hospital

A Guide for Trustees, Administrators,
and Volunteers

By Raymond P. Sloan

HARPER & ROW, PUBLISHERS   NEW YORK

Contents

Preface

THE SPOTLIGHT of public attention is being turned upon hospitals as focal points of the nation's health facilities. To evaluate fairly the services these institutions offer requires wider understanding of the problems involved in the wise and efficient operation of a modern hospital. The purpose of this book is to present a concise picture of the American hospital system with an explanation of changes that are necessary to meet present and future health needs.

For the average American, modern hospital service is a commodity he purchases under compulsion, and at prices beyond his comprehension. Any questions regarding the size of his hospital bill are countered with the assurance that he is benefitting from the highest standards of hospital care in the world—and on his next visit his bill may be even higher.

It is important that the public understand the hospital story—the auspices under which these institutions operate, their financing, their management patterns and functions, their participation in education and research, the reason for the high costs of their services. It is a story of big business—the fourth largest of all American industries.

The following pages are addressed as well to those directly involved in health and hospital care—both laymen and professional participants. I have sought to give particular attention to the functions and responsibilities of trustees, and the importance of their orientation. The book undertakes also to describe the role of the doctor as a member of the hospital team, new concepts of executive direction as practiced by the administrator, and the potentials of auxiliary members and volunteers.

It is beyond the physical scope of this or any other single volume to include all the answers. It can hope only to outline and to promote interest in exploring further the complexities of hospital operation. My purpose is to measure the progress that has been made, to establish a true picture of the modern hospital as a community health center, dedicated not merely to the practice of preventive medicine and the care of the sick, but to education and research.

Such basic facts, I hope, may encourage further study of a health system that, notwithstanding its many virtues, needs to be critically appraised and revised to meet not only today's requirements but also those of the years to come.

It would be impossible to express appreciation to all those who have helped to produce this volume. These include numerous local, state, regional, and national associations that have graciously invited me to participate in their meetings. The friendship and allegiance of many hospital trustees, administrators, and medical staff members have contributed materially to the substance of the book. Finally, there are long-time friends and associates without whose encouragement and counsel this book would not have been written. To the following I express particular thanks: C. Rufus Rorem, Ph.D., C.P.A., special consultant, Hospital Review and Planning Council of Southern New York, Inc.; Joseph Peters, assistant executive director, Hospital Review and Planning Council of Southern New York, Inc.; Clement C. Clay, M.D., professor of administrative medicine, Columbia University; Sally E. Knapp, assistant professor of administrative medicine, Columbia University; Caroline Flanders, director, Women's Activity Division, United Hospital Fund of New York; Dr. Frederick T. Hill, Thayer Hospital, Waterville, Maine; and Michael Lesparre, American Hospital Association. Finally, my appreciation to James Thomas McAndrew, Jr., for the two organization charts.

New York City   **R.P.S.**
November 1, 1965

PART ONE

The American Hospital Pattern

I

Types and Services

VOLUNTARY, GOVERNMENT, AND PROPRIETARY

HOSPITAL SERVICE as we know it today differs greatly from its original form—the medieval houses of refuge for the homeless, the sick and infirm. These were ecclesiastical rather than medical institutions, placing their emphasis upon faith and love, rather than upon nursing skill and medical science.

Gradually the socially-minded church groups were joined by privileged individuals moved by the desire to do something for the needy. Such benevolence produced substantial financial support, including houses and properties which were converted to health purposes. These organizations became the prototype of the so-called "community hospital."

Once the need for such services was recognized, guilds, fraternal organizations and municipalities began to assume responsibility for health facilities. Certain doctors, too, sensing the potentialities, proceeded to establish their

3

own sanitariums for those able to pay for more personal attention.

From such modest beginnings, hospitals have developed into headquarters for health, engaged in four distinct functions—the care of the sick, public and professional education, the conduct of research, and the practice of preventive medicine. Hospital service is never static. It is constantly being improved, readjusted, and expanded to meet the demands of a changing society, with new developments in scientific equipment and techniques.

Three kinds of hospitals constitute the American pattern—voluntary, government, and proprietary. Of these three, the nonprofit, voluntary hospitals meet the major needs of our population and are largely responsible for the high standards of medical care we enjoy today.

According to recent listings in the American Hospital Association's annual directory, there are 7,028 hospitals in the United States. Of these, 3,623 are nonprofit and voluntary: this includes 1,259 sponsored by churches. Approximately 2,415 are government-owned, and 860 are proprietary.

The voluntary hospital can be best described as a public enterprise conducted under private management. It is sponsored by boards of men and women, representative of the community, who are legally and morally responsible for its professional services, properties, and policies. According to latest figures, some 800,000 individuals are serving in such capacities.

In addition to providing adequate financing, the primary obligations of trustee groups are to ensure the presence of qualified medical staffs with supporting skilled workers, competent administration, and the essential physical facilities to maintain a comprehensive program of health care predicated on community needs.

Some voluntary, nonprofit institutions are conducted under the aegis of churches, racial groups, or fraternal orders. Catholic hospitals, while operating under the control of church orders, are now broadening their support through the addition of lay advisory groups. Church affiliated institutions are generally nonsectarian in their admissions policies.

No financial gain accrues to the sponsors of the voluntary hospital, nor are they liable for debts incurred. Properly organized and operated, the corporation is exempt from federal, state, and local taxation.

Patients occupying private rooms pay a rate somewhat above actual cost. This helps meet the deficits the institution incurs in serving those who cannot afford to pay full coverage. Such policy, while subject to question in the light of present-day economics and health planning, remains a heritage of voluntary endeavor. However, as government assumes the responsibility to pay the full cost of hospital care for the indigent, the practice of having private patients pay for the less fortunate should be abandoned.

Also, to an increasing degree, healthy people are supporting our hospitals by prepaying for the care they may need. Hospitalization insurance, first introduced in 1929, now represents more than half the current income of all voluntary hospitals. Financial assistance for the care of those medically indigent from state and local government still does not always represent full coverage, unfortunately. The balance of support is derived from endowments and public appeals, conducted either as community chest drives or individual hospital fund-raising campaigns.

 Government hospitals are supported by tax funds and are sponsored by federal, state, city, or county bodies. Responsibility for management rests with an appointed or elected government official, frequently a physician who may or may not have administrative training. Occasionally an advisory board, comprising business or professional leaders, serves as management counselors.

For example, New York City's municipal hospital system comprises 21 hospitals operated by the Department of Hospitals. These fall legally under one head—the Commissioner of Hospitals. He is supported by a ten-man board made up of an equal number of lay and professional members. In addition, the majority have local boards representing community interests which serve in advisory capacities to the administrator.

Many government hospitals concentrate upon care of war veterans and the chronically ill, particularly those suffering from mental disorders and tuberculosis. Their patients pay little if anything.

 Proprietary hospitals are operated for profit and are found most frequently in communities showing a rapid population growth and still lacking benefits of voluntary hospital services. These institutions are frequently financed by doctors or other individuals who see advantages in the greater independence and flexibility of rules existing under individual control. Their founders serve as board members, controlling all policies and sharing any profits that may accrue.

Inadequate licensing laws have made it difficult to stop construction of unneeded or low standard proprietary hospitals. Many state licensure acts rely on outdated construction standards while ignoring the vital factors such as the need for the proposed facilities and the type of ownership. Minimal standards are now being sought in certain areas.

"GENERAL" VS. "SPECIAL" HOSPITALS

HOSPITAL SERVICES fall into two classifications— "general," which provides care for patients suffering from a variety of diseases, and "special" which treats specific maladies. In the latter group are children's hospitals and ones specializing in eye, ear, nose, and throat diseases, cancer, tuberculosis, mental and nervous disorders, and long term illness. Communicable disease hospitals and convalescent homes are similarly classified. The trend is away from the "special disease" hospital and toward the "general" hospital assuming responsibility directly or indirectly for all physical or mental disabilities. All patients can benefit from the comprehensive services and facilities available in the general hospital.

Hospital size is rated by the bed capacity for which the building was originally designed; it does not include beds added in hallways or other spaces. Buildings of 100 beds and less are classified as *Small,* and some 57 per cent of the country's hospitals fall into this classification. Hospitals from 100 to 300 beds are *Medium Size.* Those with 300 to 1,000 and more beds are *Large.*

Newborn infants' bassinets are figured separately on the basis that it is the mother who is the patient. The infant remains a boarder unless his physical condition requires his transferal to another department.

In short-term hospitals, those offering acute care, the average length of stay has dropped in recent years from 9.1 days to 7.6 days. In those long-term institutions which provide care for patients with chronic conditions or illnesses, more extended periods of treatment are required.

The degree to which hospitals are occupied is known as "percentage of occupancy." An average annual occupancy of 80 per cent is considered optimum use. Anything above that figure is regarded as abnormally high.

Wide fluctuation is expected in maternity occupancy, thus making that service uneconomical. Seasonal variances also seriously effect hospital finances. Most institutions, other than those in resort areas, are less crowded during the summer due to doctors' vacation schedules. Almost universally the variation is downward by about 15 per cent over weekends and 10 per cent during the heavy vacation months.

The empty bed is, for the hospital, the most expensive bed and requires maintenance without compensating income. $8,000 to $10,000 per year is the estimated cost for maintenance alone, including such services as nursing personnel, linen supplies, etc. As in industry where the idle machine is the most costly, so in hospitals the empty bed costs almost as much to maintain as one that is occupied.

Attention is being focused today upon the importance of investigating possible abuses by the over-utilization of hospital facilities. Over-utilization increases hospital costs by requiring greater capital investment to provide more beds. It does not always reflect "over-stay." It may result from unnecessary admissions, and overuse of drugs, x-ray, laboratory facilities, etc. Also, unnecessary facilities and services boost hospital insurance rates.

HEALTH CARE PATTERNS

A VARIATION from the traditional pattern of community health service is the so-called "group practice" clinic. Here, formal group organization frequently centers on a general physician who establishes patient contacts and acts as a referral agent. With specialists in several fields he is employed on a full-time basis. Frequently the physicians pool their incomes as well as their expenses, and patients pay the group or clinic rather than the doctor they have consulted. In certain instances all doctors' fees above their established salaries go into the hospital treasury.

Some group plans give comprehensive service for a stipulated fee. Among the notable examples are the Henry Ford Hospital, Detroit; Mary Hitchcock Memorial Hospital, Hanover, N. H; the Mayo Clinic, Rochester, Minn.; and the Lahey Clinic, Boston. Others give service on a prepayment basis. Such group practice units were sponsored originally by industrial plants, farm groups, or labor unions. Included among these are the Kaiser Permanente Clinic, Oakland, Calif.; the Ross-Loos Clinic, Los Angeles; and Trinity Hospital, Little Rock, Ark.

More recently community enterprises have developed organizational patterns similar to that of the Health Insurance Plan of Greater New York. Begun in 1947 this voluntary medical care plan is incorporated under the state insurance law as a nonprofit agency, with about thirty neighborhood group practice centers that render all medical services in the offices of the group, in the hospital, or in the patient's home, with professional eligibility being the responsibility of a medical board. Each group employs general physicians and specialists, many of whom are diplomaes of American specialty boards and are serving on the staffs of approved hospitals. Each group operates through a central administrative office.

"Group practice" is actually medical partnership, and is based on the old adage that two heads are better than one. Such practice has effectively demonstrated the importance of coordinating the knowledge and skills of specialists and general practitioners in one program.

Out-patient departments or clinics were originally known as dispensaries or health stations. Services were available to those who could pay little or nothing. Today, recognized as the "family doctor" for the indigent, they are being reorganized and expanded to meet broader needs.

The out-patient department in modern guise constitutes

a screening process through which patients pass before being admitted to the hospital. Proper diagnosis, treatment, and follow-up in an out-patient clinic may eliminate the need for hospitalization or decrease the length of the hospital stay. This is in line with current emphasis on the treatment of people on an ambulatory basis.

While not all medical men assume clinic responsibility, many are sufficiently dedicated to devote certain hours to sustain the patient load without financial recompense. In large institutions staff organization requires a full-time out-patient or clinic director. More frequently the work is carried on by younger physicians who benefit from the experience and augment their private incomes by working on a part-time salary basis. In government hospitals the clinic patient pays nothing and in voluntary hospitals the charge is nominal. At best such public service contributes to the total hospital operating deficit.

Emphasis upon ambulatory care is also illustrated by the expanding use of emergency departments. The great majority of cases so treated are not traumatic or even true emergencies. Many patients use emergency facilities because they do not have to wait for service as in the out-patient department, because out-patient hours are inconvenient, or their private physicians are not available.

Despite the suspicion of certain staff members that this use of emergency departments reflects further disposition on the part of hospitals to "take over," planning groups envision the accident room of tomorrow will include, in addition to surgeries, rest and observation facilities which will ultimately reduce hospital admissions.

Continuity in the hospital program is being studied to assure better care at reasonable costs. "Progressive patient care" is a new concept of service adopted in whole or in part by numerous institutions. Although its effect on costs has not been convincing it has demonstrated benefits for the patient, the hospital, and the community.

In its entirety the plan embraces five areas of service— intensive care, intermediate care, self-care, long-term care and home care.

Patients, critically ill, are concentrated in one area under the supervision of specially trained nurses and attendants. Ambulatory patients still unable to return home are assigned to an intermediate unit. Self-care approximates hotel accommodations and is for those who need only diagnostic or convalescent attentions. Long-term care is for those requiring daily attention unattainable at home. Finally, there is a completely organized home care program.

Some patients can be taken care of as well or even better in their homes at less than one-fourth the cost of bed care in the hospital. Although chiefly directed toward convalescents and elderly persons, it applies as well to patients of all ages.

Mobile hospital service provides all facilities but those available only in the hospital. The organizational set-up of such service depends upon the size and nature of the hospital and the community, and many other factors. It may range all the way from a visiting-nurse service to a more complete department headed by a staff physician who serves on a full-time basis and medical service provided

by staff physicians and part-time consultants. A typical
pattern is the coordinated team of physicians, nurses,
social workers, clerical staff, physical therapists, occupational therapists, and housekeeping aides. While dietetics
is not commonly included due to a general shortage of
dietitians, its importance to the program is recognized.

Homestead programs, less frequently encountered, help
meet the needs of the chronically disabled in congenial
surroundings under hospital direction. Emphasis is placed
upon recreational facilities. Maintenance and medical
supervision are the responsibility of a specially assigned
physician.

Because of its voluntary structure the American hospital pattern is unique. With limited government support
and a minimum of government intervention, it has provided the public with a high level of health care. Notwithstanding its achievements, certain questions are
developing in the public mind, particularly among representatives of organized labor, prompted mainly by the
steadily mounting costs. To answer these questions and
to eliminate doubts requires a careful reappraisal of the
prevailing organizations.

2

New Departures

NEW CONCEPTS

IN SHARP CONTRAST to the original function of concentrating upon acute conditions, the hospital of today, and to a greater degree the hospital of tomorrow, must assume responsibility for overall public health. This is an outgrowth of changing living habits, population trends, age spans, and the types of diseases that befall us. Communities and neighborhoods are changing and hospitals must be prepared to meet new needs.

It is reasonable to visualize the hospital serving as headquarters for the local or county health department, visiting nurse group, or tuberculosis, venereal disease, maternal and child health services, while also working closely with cancer prevention programs, humane societies, and children's courts. These latter affiliations offer fewer problems in small communities where patterns of living are less complex.

Mental health is now recognized as a vital part of total comprehensive medical care and alcoholism requires scientific treatment. Convalescence, rehabilitation, long-term illness, and the care of geriatrics all now fall within the jurisdiction of the general community hospital.

Greater attention must be given to community and area-wide planning of hospital and health services. Personal interests must be subjugated on behalf of better health standards and cooperation is more vital than competition.

The effects of isolationism are unhappily demonstrated by one hospital of sixty beds specializing in children's diseases located within short distance of a large teaching hospital in a metropolitan area. Founded some forty years ago, the hospital is still run by members of the same family, dominating a self-perpetuating board—a world unto itself with no disposition to pool resources at a substantial reduction of costs.

In another section of the country an institution with an excellent reputation for research on cardiac children has extravagantly added general care beds in competition with three other hospitals within a radius of 15 or 20 miles.

The happier side of the picture reveals one planning agency which succeeded in removing some 1,500 beds during the first weeks of its existence from the contemplated expansion programs of its member institutions without impairing health services. This represented operational savings of some $15 million dollars annually, to say nothing of original construction costs.

In one of the larger New England cities an institution of 160 beds operating under Catholic auspices has joined another general hospital of 300 beds in developing a mutual advanced training program for medical school graduates. This program is headed by a medical director. Ten doctors act as coordinators and more than 50 physicians serve as teachers. Through such coordination the necessary variety of patients, equipment, and facilities for an outstanding medical education program are assured. Although benefits from the program in terms of dollars are difficult to estimate, the relatively expensive emergency coverage of some community hospitals has been eliminated through the presence of a house staff working in conjunction with regular staff members. Another area of affiliation between these two hospitals is a joint professional library committee. Its responsibility is to develop a cooperative relationship between the two libraries and reduce to a minimum any duplications in volumes and services. Uniform credit and collection policies form a third mutual endeavor. This includes pre-admission data, deposits (depending upon insurance coverage), assignment of insurance benefits, evaluation of ability to pay, interim and discharge billing, and delinquent account follow-up.

Coordination and affiliation no longer are considered words of threat; they hold promise of more inclusive patterns of health care with greater control of costs. Central laundries, group purchasing, among other joint projects, are becoming common.

More drastic is the recent trend of hospital mergers. Most noteworthy of all perhaps, are those that have taken place in the metropolitan area of New York. Close affiliation of large teaching centers with municipal hospitals has materially up-graded the health care of New York. Sixteen such coordination programs are already in effect with assurance that others will follow.

According to Dr. Ray E. Trussell, Director of the School of Public Health and Administrative Medicine at Columbia and a former commissioner of the New York City Department of Hospitals,

The hospital of the future will be increasingly the hub of health services provided by a variety of agencies and professions, because of the growing complexity of medical care. The hospital will assume responsibility also for related services, for diagnostic and other procedures and for a greater variety of psychiatric services in the hospital and in the community.

On the regional and state level, citizens, sometimes voluntarily and other times by government appointment, are seeing what can be done to coordinate health facilities and to reduce costs through the organization of area-wide hospital planning councils. The function of such groups is to conduct surveys of a region's existing health resources and then to make recommendations for supplementation, restriction, or coordination based on present needs and potential growth. They decide which institutions should be replaced or modernized. They study the problems of others that because of size or inadequate facilities are unable to provide comprehensive health care.

In the words of Dr. C. Rufus Rorem, leader in community hospital planning and former executive director of the Hospital Planning Association of Allegheny County, Pa.,

Coordination does not imply reduction of autonomy in management or opporunity to excel in standards of professional service. On the contrary, awareness of community needs and the programs of other hospitals enables each institution to realize its potential through a distinct service which adds to the general welfare.

Coordinated health planning is just as essential to the economic and cultural development of a community as an efficient transportation, public safety, educational or welfare program. It is the function of a hospital planning agency to achieve more effective use of total health personnel and facilities in the area where it is established.

Government is, and will continue exerting greater control over the country's health program. Hospital trustees, administrators, and medical staff members would do well to recognize this fact. No one can deny that voluntary sponsorship has provided high standards of medical care. Yet, increasing government participation is inevitable. Besides offering financial aid in new building construction, it assumes responsibility for standards in the hospitals it licenses as well as those that care for patients at public expense. Good judgment dictates working with government, not against it.

To avoid the threat of government *domination* a well organized line of defense by hospital groups is essential. Physicians, particularly, need to be more closely identified with area-wide planning and medical care programs, and to participate in efforts to control and reduce hospital costs. The voluntary team approach, its objectives clearly defined and its strengths demonstrated, should put hospitals in a position to negotiate successfully with government on behalf of community health.

COMMUNITY PLANNING COUNCILS

CHANGING POPULATION TRENDS, demands for broader community health services, modern developments in medical science, and the need to control costs have created an awareness of the importance of over-all hospital planning.

Some hospital boards have been insular in their thinking; each ambitious that his institution possess every modern facility and piece of equipment. There has been a tendency, also, to over-emphasize general hospital beds, with little, if any, provision for other important health services, such as care of the long-term patient, the ambulatory patient, the mentally ill, and those requiring long-term rehabilitation.

Duplication and overlapping of services contributes to rising costs. This has led to the organization of more planning councils conducted on state, regional, or city levels.

The concept of collective planning on a state-wide basis received added impetus through the enactment of the Hospital Survey and Construction Act 9, Public Law 725 of the 79th Congress, which requires the development of state plans. This does not dictate the extent to which individual institutions should subscribe to overall planning, but it specifies needs and priorities for additional beds and services.

The New York State Hospital Review and Planning Council is an example of planning at the state level. This operates within the State Department of Health and comprises 31 individuals who are representative of the public, including at least one member nominated by each of seven regional councils recognized by the state body. Provisions are made for suitable representation by physicians and persons engaged in hospital or nursing home activities. Appointment is made by the governor. However, no individual can be a member for more than six years in any period of twelve consecutive years.

The seven regional councils are: Hospital Review and Planning Council of Western New York, Inc.; Rochester Regional Hospital Council, Inc.; Review and Planning Council of Central New York, Inc.; Regional Review and Planning Council of Northeastern New York, Inc.; Northern Metropolitan Regional Hospital Review and Planning Council; Long Island Regional Hospital Review and Planning Council; and the Hospital Review and Planning Council of Southern New York. This last one covers the five metropolitan areas of New York City and nine counties in adjacent areas.

The state council in cooperation with regional groups considers application for establishment of new institutions and for expansion or substantial modification of existing facilities. Subject to approval of the commissioner of health, the council is also empowered to establish requirements for uniform cost reporting, medical audits, reimbursement for hospital services, and standards of hospital operation.

Hospital and health care planning at the county level is demonstrated by the Hospital Planning Association of Allegheny County, Pittsburgh, Pennsylvania, and the Monroe County Patient Care Planning Council, Rochester, New York.

The Allegheny Association had its origin in a study made in 1957 by the Hospital Council of Western Pennsylvania. At that time practically every community hospital in the county was planning substantial capital expansion, without knowledge of other programs or consideration of the community's requirements.

A board of directors was selected, with preference for those recognized as civic leaders, rather than as experts in the hospital or health field. These individuals assemble quarterly to act on recommendations made by a ten-man executive committee, which meets monthly. Expenses of the program are met through contributions from industrial and commercial corporations maintaining headquarters in the county.

According to Dr. Rorem who was successful in getting the Pennsylvania group off to a good start,

The Hospital Planning Association has no legal authority to control a hospital's services or expansion of plant or equipment. It cannot compel a hospital to restrict its services against the wishes of its staff and board of directors. This very lack of legal authority permits the Association to study health problems with objectivity and to propose imaginative solutions. The Association's overall concern is with service to the total community whose members pay the bills for "upkeep" as well as the "first cost" of health facilities. Community needs come first, even if sometimes they conflict with the desires and hopes of hospital representatives.

The Monroe County Patient Care Planning Council in New York State was formed at the request of a group of six Rochester community agencies to coordinate over-all health planning in the county. It was set up by 20 people, who firmly believed that uncoordinated plans to replace or modernize several hospitals would be beyond the financial resources of the community. These individuals included representatives from the county and city governments, the County Health Office, the President of the Hospital Council, Dean of the Medical School, and representatives from labor, the Medical Society, Community Chest, Council of Social Agencies, Industrial Management Council, New York State Department of Health, etc.

The first objective of the Council was to survey with teams of doctors the bed utilization of the seven hospitals involved. It was soon discovered that about 20 per cent of the beds were occupied by patients who could have been cared for in other facilities, had they been available.

In consequence, instead of adding 500 acute general beds, 252 unsuitable beds in the various hospitals were eliminated and replaced with suitable beds. This meant that only 140 new acute beds were necessary, leaving new extended care beds to be constructed in suitable units at three of the hospitals.

Unnecessary duplication of services and equipment requires careful study. This does not mean that several hospitals should not have all necessary facilities or render essential services. It applies solely to those institutions installing expensive equipment, or providing costly services that are infrequently used.

Accusing fingers are sometimes pointed at area-wide planning as discouraging to individual initiative. Ample evidence is available, nevertheless, to prove that no agency operating independently can meet the complexities of total health care. Only through partnership with other health facilities can this be successfully accomplished.

The true value of functional planning for health services is outlined in the report of the Joint Committee of the American Hospital Association and the United States Public Health Service, entitled "Area-wide Planning for Hospitals and Related Health Facilities."

Although good health services cannot be purchased cheaply, sound planning will forestall unwarranted costs and elevate the level of today's health care.

According to the report,

Through area-wide planning, local agencies can help to:

Maintain and improve quality of care as economically as possible.

Correct deficiencies in existing facilities and services.

Stimulate the construction of needed facilities, including those for educational purposes.

Discourage construction not conforming to community needs.

Assure more effective use of community funds by avoiding unnecessary duplication of highly specialized, infrequently used expensive facilities.

Improve patient care by developing more effective interrelationships among facilities.

Develop an orderly distribution of all facilities in keeping with the projected population characteristics and the overall community development.

Encourage individual facilities to define and carry out their objectives and projected roles in relation to other facilities, services and community needs.

Stimulate facilities to recognize opportunities for better coordination of services.

Demonstrate the need for philanthropic and public funds through a well-developed information program.

Meeting public health needs on a coordinated community basis may involve sacrifice for some individuals. It can mean loss of an identity so proudly cherished during the years. It can mean delegating to oblivion building plans already on the drawing boards. The compensation is the satisfaction of maintaining the best community health standards.

3

How Our Hospitals Function

THE MANAGEMENT PATTERN

THE MANAGEMENT PATTERN of our hospitals is complex. With the exception of proprietary ones, hospitals constitute an important public utility operated without financial gain. Their position in the community and their reputation as health centers providing education and research in addition to patient care, depends upon the close collaboration of individuals of widely divergent backgrounds. Their goals can be accomplished only through a strong management team comprising the governing board, the administration, and the medical staff.

The hospital organization pattern, involves two broad functions—the formation of policies and their administration. Obviously the organization chart reflects the size and the character of the institution's services. Hospitals affiliated with a university or medical school have more complex management patterns than the average community hospital. In the former, several officers may be involved, an executive vice-president, an educator, and a hospital director.

Because the nonprofit voluntary hospital renders a majority of the health care in the United States, its organizational structure deserves particular attention. Some of these institutions are established as separate units incorporated and chartered by the state. Others are subsidiaries of existing religious, fraternal, educational, or charitable organizations operating under the charter of the parent body.

Members of a nonprofit corporation make no money from its operations, nor are they liable for any debts incurred. Properly organized and operated, the corporation is exempt fom federal and frequently from state and local taxation. Reference should be made to the model Constitution and Bylaws for a Voluntary Hospital, prepared by the American Hospital Association. Competent legal counsel is also important.

Hospital corporations vary in scope of service. In some, the governing board is virtually self-perpetuating; in others, the corporation adheres more closely to business practice and the required number of members is elected.

Memberships are sometimes provided through financial contributions to the work by forming groups known as "Friends of the Hospital," or "Society of the Hospital." Bylaws include charter members, life or sustaining members and annual members. These incorporators elect members to the governing board.

Sometimes corporate membership is made possible by a plan through which a majority of the members who represent various community organizations are specified *ex officio*. These individuals then select the remaining members from the community at large.

Hospital organization charts have one point in common —a board of directors that acts as a framework for operational procedures. Business and professional responsibilities are defined in the bylaws and their execution is assigned to committees concerned with overall operation rather than with specific details. From the board and its executive committee authority descends through the administrator to various standing committees of the board with a direct line between the administrator and the auxiliary or volunteer groups. Also from the board, authority passes through the administrator and the joint conference committee to the medical staff.

The medical staff is self-governing and has its own bylaws, rules, and regulations, as recommended by the Joint Commission on Accreditation of Hospitals and the American Hospital Association. Such bylaws are subject to the approval of the trustees.

The governing board is legally and morally responsible for the quality of the hospital's medical care. It appoints the staff.

Appointment to the medical staff of a voluntary hospital is a privilege granted by the governing board, and not a right which the physician may demand. In making the appointment and specifying the limitations of the physician's practice, the governing board usually follows the recommendations of the appropriate committees of the medical staff.

Reporting directly to the administrator or his assistants are the heads of such departments as pathology, radiology,

CHART I. ORGANIZATION OF AVERAGE-SIZED VOLUNTARY HOSPITAL

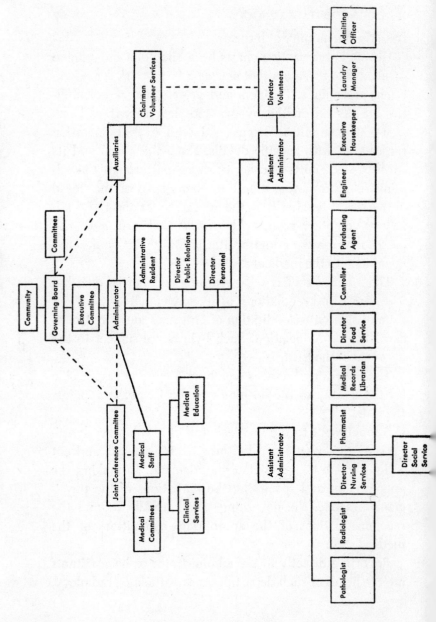

nursing service and nursing education, pharmacology, medical records library—dietary, controller, purchasing, engineering, housekeeping, laundry, and admissions.

Because the department of nursing constitutes a major service and employs a substantial percentage of the personnel, it deserves special notice. The director of nursing service is accountable to the administrator. In the larger hospitals with extensive programs, two directors may be required to assume joint responsibility for patient care, nursing education and discipline. In some hospitals the director of nursing and the controller are called the assistant administrator.

The administrator, in addition to exercising control over departmental operation, serves as counsellor to the board in developing planning programs affecting the hospital and its relationship to other community health agencies. He formulates closely coordinated groups of medical men and other professional workers whose goal is high standards of health care. He is the middle man between the board and the medical staff, the board and the patient, and the board and the public. He interprets hospital functions to the board, the medical staff, the personnel, and the community, and develops educational programs to encourage coordination on the part of all concerned.

Such broad powers require exceptional qualifications and training. A master's degree in hospital administration is rapidly becoming a requisite for those seeking such appointments.

Despite the fact that the administrator is the central figure in hospital management, certain factors can develop to threaten his position. These may take the form of an over dominant board president or an ambitious medical staff member. Such tendencies without strict control can injure the management pattern.

Tremendous advances have been made since the days when hospital services were regarded principally as philanthropic endeavor. To an increasing extent the broader health facilities that hospitals now offer are acknowledged as big business with the following basic variance: the hospital goal is patient care; the goal of business is to make a profit. Hospital operation achieves its purpose if losses are held within reasonable limits and the hospital can remain solvent.

The question is: How far can hospitals go in establishing more efficient forms of organization and executive direction at no loss of personal motivation or involvement? A closely coordinated management team is the answer: a team having a board of trustees at the policy making level devoted to developing a chain of comprehensive community health services. At the management level is an administrator of true executive caliber who may carry the title of president or executive vice-president. Rendering the actual service is a medical staff adhering to professional standards and serving as a counsellor in medical affairs. Each of these groups complements the others in meeting over all community health needs.

OFFICERS AND BOARD

A HOSPITAL has as its officers a president, vice-president, secretary, and treasurer. Assistants are frequently provided to insure continuity should anyone fail to participate.

The president's functions parallel those of a chairman of the board of a business corporation. He serves as the major representative of the sponsoring group. He is the liaison officer between the administrator and the board and also between hospital and the community. He presides over all board meetings and serves ex officio on its various committees.

The president's tenure of office depends upon the type of corporate structure, the community, and the availability of suitable talent. It may extend from one to twenty or more years. Silver anniversaries are not unusual in hospital history.

One year is hardly enough to enable an individual to exert the proper direction even with training resulting from other executive responsibilities. Furthermore, too frequent changes in personality and social concepts can add to the problems.

The one-man show that continues for an indefinite run can also be a handicap. Fresh ideas are essential, and new faces offer assurance of broadening interest and popular support.

It is not unusual to find hospitals whose policies have been dominated by one family for 50 years or more. Five or six years is a reasonable term of service for the hospital president, with ten as a maximum. Flexibility, so essential in meeting local situations can be accomplished through annual elections.

The vice-president substitutes for the president when necessary, and the secretary serves both the corporation, where such a body exists, and the governing board. The treasurer, in conjunction with the finance committee is custodian of the hospital's funds.

Appointment of officers and directors is made on recommendation and action taken by the corporation, or if the enterprise is more closely held, by the governing board on the recommendation of a nominating committee. Officers generally serve one year.

Many hospital bylaws stipulate boards that are virtually self-perpetuating. Long and loyal association is desirable, unless it stands in the way of broader community involvements.

Greater democracy is assured by placing certain limitations on trustee service. Some hospitals establish five-, three-, or two-year terms with reelection possible for a second term. One common procedure is to stipulate two terms of three years each, permitting the individual to continue his participation following a year's leave of absence.

To offset the possibility of losing the trustee's allegiance during his layoff term he may be retained without voting power, or be given some special assignment. Such a situation has been met successfully by appointing the retiring member as chairman of a long term planning committee or assigning him to certain ad hoc committees.

To promote community support while keeping the board within workable limits, a supplementary group is sometimes established. Its members, properly oriented, serve as friends and advisors and may eventually make effective trustees.

A three-stage plan may provide an alternative to cover the entire gamut of trustee service. This establishes a junior group oriented to assume eventually full responsibility, the board itself, and an honorary body to serve as counsellors.

No fixed retirement age applies to hospital board members. A trustee with a distinguished record of service may find it difficult to remain active, yet he is as reluctant to withdraw as the institution is to have him do so. Honorary groups of "elder statesmen" have met such situations successfully by having their members serve as sources of referral, but without definite obligations.

Such transition from active service to semi-retirement needs to be handled with discretion as one president discovered. Having convinced a formerly active member that he should accept "honorary rank," it seemed only fitting to pay him proper tribute. Following the announcement of his change of status at the annual meeting the recipient of the praise was so gratified that stepping up to the president he remarked—"You know, Ed, after hearing you tell about what I mean to this fine institution, I believe I'd better stay on the active list."

What is the ideal size of the hospital board? The most succinct answer to this question is one large enough to be representative of the community, yet small enough to be efficient. Numbers range from 7 to 58 but from 7 to 17 members form an ideal number. Where large boards exist the major share of the work is done by an executive committee. Advocates of large boards emphasize the prestige and importance of influential names, to say nothing of the funds derived from such sources.

To encourage public interest, yet uphold the obligations of trusteeship a society of friends of the hospital may be the answer. This provides latitude for window dressing yet restricts board membership to active participation.

STANDING AND AD HOC COMMITTEES

COMMITTEES FORM THE BACKGROUND of the hospital's management pattern by providing an outlet for members' skills and qualifications. They facilitate the process by which the board reaches its decisions and expedite legislative procedures.

It should be written in the bylaws that the administrator serves *ex officio* on all committees including those of the medical staff. Under favorable circumstances hospital committees prove a help to both board and administration. They stimulate action, advice, and opinion. They encourage involvement in the institution's affairs. Poorly organized ones, however, become a crutch to weak and indecisive board performance. Naming one more committee and hoping it will produce the right answer fools only those involved. Add to this ineffective chairmanship, strong differences of opinion, unprecise timing, and the results are obvious.

The hospital's size, type of service, and organization plan will influence the number of members on the committees. A good rule to follow is—"the fewer committees the better, and make the few good." If, for example, one executive committee seems adequate for the small hospital there is no need for others. Furthermore, committees should generally be limited in size to from three to seven members. Beyond that they become unwieldy.

Many institutions suffer from "committeeitis." Such groups have a way of multiplying and usually are recognized only by name. One hospital board discovered it had 17 committees, many of them inactive for years.

Present trends are best met by certain standing committees covering areas of operation demanding continuous attention. Ad hoc committees can be appointed as required to study specific problems such as building and expansion programs, labor negotiations, or special services. One institution recognized the importance of orienting trustees to their responsibilities for the quality of medical care, and established an ad hoc committee to give board members a background in medical staff organization and an understanding of some of the technical aspects of medicine. Once the objectives of such groups are attained the committee is usually abandoned.

One question every hospital might well consider: Is the existing committee structure sufficiently flexible to meet changing conditions in the health field and also to provide ample opportunity for participation by business leaders and others?

Some institutions are reorganizing their committee framework on the basis of various areas of responsibility such as finance, planning, management and patient care, community and governmental relations, medical staff relations, and education. There is no standard by which committee services are identified. In one institution a house committee may assume responsibility solely for the maintenance and repair of the physical property. In another, the house committee may deal with internal affairs such as medical staff appointments, rules, and regulations. The following standing committees are common: executive, joint conference, finance, education, public relations, personnel, long term planning, building and grounds, and nominating.

The executive committee, at the top, serves as the right hand of the governing board. Its size enables it to be called for emergency action on short notice at any time. Under such circumstances it functions for the board, having been granted ad interim powers. This committee is accountable for the achievement of the hospital's objectives, interprets and defines policies, programs, and procedures determined by the board. Ideally it should work closely with the administrator and support him.

Officers of the board plus others chosen for special reasons frequently comprise the membership of the executive committee; or, the president may serve with the chairmen of other standing committees. In any event such appointments should be based on individual talent and abilities with recognition of the time involved.

The board president usually serves as chairman, but the presiding officer may be elected. Most executive committees meet once a month, others on call, while only a small percentage gather weekly.

The joint conference committee forms an important communications bridge between the medical staff, the board of trustees, and the administrator. Despite the fact that the physician supplies the service for which the hospital is responsible, he seldom has any voice in its management and long term planning. The board member, on the other hand, who carries a major share of the financial burden has little contact with the miracles taking place through the skill of the doctors in whose appointment he has participated. To assure mutual appreciation of the overall picture close relationships are essential at policy, administrative, and professional levels.

Occasionally the joint conference committee appears under some title such as Medical Advisory Committee, or Committee of Professional and Medical Affairs. Commonly it is made up of an equal number of trustees and medical staff members with the administrator serving *ex officio*. In a very small hospital membership may include the entire staff and board of trustees. A joint conference committee in some form is requisite for accreditation by the Joint Commission on Accreditation of Hospitals. This committee reports and makes recommendations to the board concerning the appointment, advancement, retirement, or dismissal of staff members. Any by-laws, rules, or regulations proposed by the staff for its own government are cleared by this committee before presentation to the full board. Its broader concepts include educational opportunities for both doctors and trustees. Through its discussions the trustee learns of medical needs and policies while the physician is initiated into financial and administrative problems.

Because finances represent a major trustee responsibility the finance committee is vital. Among its duties are preparing a sound financial program, reviewing the budget, serving as counselor to the board on the investment of endowment or reserve funds, making loans, and handling real estate and physical properties. This group must take steps to provide the necessary funds to meet the budget, secure adequate sums from local government agencies for the care of the indigent, review the financial reports submitted by the chief executive, and make suitable recommendations to the board.

In large institutions, in addition to the finance committee, a budget committee may be appointed to concentrate upon figures projected by the administrator and to determine how they may be met. Similarly, certain hospitals relieve the finance committee from sole responsibility in investing funds by employing a financial counselor.

Constant vigilance is required over the financial portfolio, necessitating regular meetings of the committee in charge and special study on occasion. For this reason inability of the finance committee chairman or member to attend regularly routine board meetings is condoned on the basis that he is doing his share.

A committee on education is increasingly valuable for hospitals that assume the functions of teaching institutions.

With nursing now only one facet of the hospital's educational program, an education committee is frequently encountered. In addition to nursing training, this committee assumes a responsibility for educational programs for staff physicians and officers as well as for the general medical profession. Increasing numbers of institutions as previously indicated are appointing directors of medical education either on a full- or part-time basis.

Public relations has become essential in providing the public with a concept of comprehensive community health service and deserves board attention. The objective should be a sound program that will integrate the hospital with the life of the community it serves. The conduct and operation of the institution has a direct bearing upon public opinion and it is essential that the members of this committee work closely with administration. In large institutions this entails the aid of a full-time development director. Such a relationship furnishes the trustee with an insight into hospital procedure while at the same time allows evaluation of public reaction. Consequently it serves as excellent orientation, particularly for the new member.

A comparative newcomer among hospital standing committees, the personnel committee assumes responsibility for an area long neglected. Hospitals for the most part have paid substandard wages and in consequence have had many substandard employees. Growing threats of or-

ganized labor, particularly in certain metropolitan centers, have become actualities with demonstrations ensuing
which threatened patient care. Administrators and trustees have been unprepared for such undisciplined action.
Today's personnel committee appraises the local situation with an eye to present and future demands. It might
well study successful hospital management practice elsewhere. Salary and wage scales for comparable services
need to be reviewed, with similar study and action on
pension plans, health coverage, vacation schedules and
other fringe benefits, workmen's compensation, and
human relations. Such a committee serves in the capacity
of counselor to the administrator, the board, and the personnel director on matters pertaining to collective bargaining and union demands. It can also provide a real
opportunity for trustees knowledgeable in labor relations.

Many hospitals have expanded at will to meet developing needs, but with little attempt to visualize a goal of
comprehensive health care. In consequence, they suffer
from the effects of poorly conceived and executed facilities which prove a handicap to sound economic management.

Such lack of foresight is now causing numerous hospital
boards to establish planning committees whose purpose is
to study each individual institution and its community as
well as neighboring hospitals and health care facilities. It develops short- and long-range plans indicating the
action necessary to insure that each institution serves its
proper function in meeting community health needs.

Such a committee becomes increasingly important in

applying for funds available through the Hill-Burton program for the renovation or replacement of existing facilities. In directing such efforts, strong leadership on the part of the administrator is essential. It is wise to seek opinion from local planning councils, professional consultants, and others qualified to conduct surveys and to make recommendations based on population trends, projected community needs, and required services.

A building and grounds committee sometimes appears in the guise of a house and property group. Its purpose is to work with the administration by supervising the maintenance, renovating, and remodeling of the hospital plant. Where substantial building planning and construction is involved an ad hoc or special committee is frequently appointed to handle the numerous details.

Other standing committees occasionally encountered are the social service committee, purchasing or insurance committee, and a legal committee. An old timer among such groups is the "visiting" or so-called "inspection" committees. "Inspection" now falls under the jurisdiction of professional counselors. This does not, however, detract from the importance of hospital visiting by board members and others as a means of learning the wonders of modern techniques and scientific equipment.

There must be justification for the standing committee and it must remain active. Standing committees assume the bulk of management responsibility. Ad hoc committees tackle specific problems requiring investigation. In recent years particularly, expanding hospital services have presented questions for which the right answers must be found. These are assigned to groups carefully selected who serve as long as the need exists.

One institution has special committees covering building construction, fire prevention, and pension plans. Others have appointed similar groups to investigate and report on medical audits, vacation schedules, and inclusive rate schedules.

While committee membership is ordinarily confined to board members, there is a growing disposition to open them to men and women of the community chosen for their knowledge or background in certain fields. Such active contacts develop interest in hospital affairs and frequently constitute material for board membership. It is possible too, that certain qualified individuals while reluctant to assume full-time obligations are willing to accept part-time assignments. Serving on one special committee charged with investigating fire prevention are a fire insurance executive and the fire chief along with two board members.

Committee responsibilities properly administered tie the hospital more closely to its community. Meetings should be held as frequently as necessary to keep members informed not only about their own hospital but on health and hospital affairs in general. Once a month is common practice, with the possible elimination of a session or two during the vacation season. At all times the executive committee should remain on call.

To hold a meeting merely as a formality is not only a waste of time but positively harmful. There must be definite reasons for taking the time of the busy people who usually serve on committees or boards. They must gain satisfaction from the feeling that they are a part of the proceedings.

Poor attendance at both board and committee meetings so frequently lamented, may not be due to lack of interest so much as to poor organizational procedure. Three things are basic to good organization. First, the agenda should be carefully prepared by the administrator and the president, and sent out sufficiently in advance to acquaint members with matters to be considered. Second, the meeting should be held at an hour and a place most convenient to those participating. Third, business procedure should be expedited. One-hour-and-a-half to two hours should be sufficient for the average board meeting.

Occasionally by-laws include penalties for delinquent members such as—"following three successive absences from board meetings without adequate reason, the offender may be dropped from the records." Such punitive action however is seldom enforced.

Difficulty getting members to attend on time was encountered by Benjamin Franklin when he founded Pennsylvania Hospital in Philadelphia, reputedly the first incorporated hospital in this country. To combat this problem he passed a resolution to the effect that

. . . each member is to pay two shillings sixpence for total absence, and one shilling for not coming on time, and for every hour's absence after the fixed time, sixpence per hour, all of which fines to be disposed of as the majority may direct. The town clock or should that not strike, the watch of the oldest person present will be the standard for determining the time.

Failure to participate may not always be attributed to lack of interest. The fault may lie in poor committee structure, ineffective programing, or inadequate chairmanship.

There is unquestionable basis for the following lines (source unknown) that might well have been penned by a disillusioned hospital trustee:

> The minutes of this meeting
> Are more like hours, I swear.
> The long debates aren't heated,
> Just swollen with hot air.
>
> And numb of haunch, and wilted
> By this exhausting board,
> I rise to make a motion—
> On tiptoe to the door.

HOSPITAL COSTS AND COST CONTROL

As CUSTODIANS OF PUBLIC FUNDS, hospital heads have reason to be concerned about rising costs. Upon them rests the responsibility of justifying such rising costs and of explaining why they will reach $55 or $60 daily within the next five years. There must be evidence of an effort to control hospital expenses to the greatest extent possible.

The public has learned about hospital costs the hard way—through bills which it does not willingly receive for services it does not understand. Furthermore, figures on statements rendered have been difficult to reconcile with announcements of substantial hospital deficits. Suspicion prevails that all is not right.

High costs are the result of the number and quality of professional services offered. Greater coordination of health facilities with accompanying economies will help keep charges down. However, if the American public wishes to continue to receive the standards of hospital care to which it is accustomed, it must pay the price.

Costs are predicated on the degree of education and research conducted by hospitals: included are new laboratory techniques, increasing use of high voltage radiation in cancer therapy, developments in heart and lung surgery, more expensive drugs, introduction of new treatments including radioisotopes and the artificial kidney. In addition to the essential physical facilities for providing diagnostic and therapeutic procedures, increasing numbers of highly trained and skilled personnel must be available.

Labor constitutes from 60 to 70 percent of all hospital costs. Two to two-and-a-half employees are required for each patient. In consequence hospitals are one of the nation's largest sources of employment.

For many years hospitals were admittingly offering poor pay, nor were they distinguished for their labor relations policies. When hospitals began to reach the proportions of big business it became evident that hospital wage scales must improve. Hospital costs have mounted by 250 percent during the past twenty years. There is evidence, too, that because of the special qualifications and the numbers of employees required by hospitals, wage scales may rise even more rapidly than those of general business.

Substandard wages plus inadequate personnel policies have placed hospitals in a vulnerable position for attack. Whether one accepts it or not, collective bargaining is now part of the hospital picture. In preparation for increased activity on the part of union organizers labor relations need to be carefully appraised.

Further reason for the rising increase in costs is that hospitals are being used by more people. Today life expectancy is over 70 as compared with 47 for those born in 1900. Individuals past 55 years use three times as much hospital care as those in the 35 to 44 age group. Statisticians predict that by 1980 there will be 24.5 million people over 65.

Reducing economic barriers to prepayment plans has encouraged greater utilization of hospital facilities. Changing concepts of American life are another factor. Larger families mean more individuals to be cared for. Higher educational standards for more of our population invite scientific treatment. Finally, fear of the hospital has disappeared. Today it is recognized as a health center embracing preventive as well as acute care.

By reason of their unique management pattern, voluntary hospitals have suffered from a lack of economic control. Budget programs, while more common today than ten or twenty years ago, are not as general as they should be. Lack of uniform accounting makes it difficult to arrive at realistic cost figures and budget estimates, and therefore hard to show the public where and how its money is being spent. Plans for greater manpower utilization are often neglected. The answer to greater operational efficiencies lies in better management.

Recognizing the critical eye with which the public is scrutinizing health costs, hospitals must endeavor to determine where economies can be effected at no sacrifice to professional care. Such costs can be controlled through voluntary action. The key individuals in such efforts are the board of governors, the administration, and the medical staff.

The efficiency of certain services can be improved. Central laundry facilities for example, have proved economically sound as has joint purchasing and coordination of plant services. Some communities are studying the possibility of developing centralized laboratories.

The obsolescence of buildings contributes to high costs and failure to provide for plant replacement results in inadequate, poorly planned facilities, requiring larger numbers of workers.

Better use of existing hospital beds will reduce the need for adding new ones. Each general hospital bed costs more than $10,000 a year to operate. Between 10 and 15 per cent of the patients in general hospitals do not belong there, according to studies made. Also, not all patients require the full range of services. This is evidenced by the increasing use of progressive care. Self-care units alone can produce savings as high as $10 a day.

Below are some suggestions for more efficient use of hospital beds:

(1) Improved schedule of admissions including greater use of facilities over week-ends and vacation periods.

(2) Full development of ambulatory services with emphasis on home care, homestead programs, and neighboring nursing home facilities.

(3) Reduced length of patient stay. This requires a proper functioning, staff-accepted utilization committee considering among other possibilities screening patients through tests before admission. Extending Blue Cross coverage to facilities other than those offered by acute general hospitals would free expensive hospital beds.

Rising costs are accompanied by rate increases for prepayment plans, Blue Cross, and health insurance plans sponsored by private organizations. This reflects the increased charges for hospital expenses. These spiraling costs, particularly as they affect older people with moderate incomes, are responsible for the introduction of the Medicare Bill.

Hospitals are incurring additional substantial expenses in the fields of education and research. Their educational programs include the training of nurses, interns, and technicians. This raises a question of whether nurses cannot be trained as effectively under the community college two-year associate degree programs. Hospital research should be subsidized by foundation and other grants.

The Surgeon General's Consultant Group on Nursing[*]

[*] "Report of the Surgeon General's Consultant Group of Nursing Toward Quality in Nursing, Needs and Goals," (U.S. Public Health

has estimated that to meet the needs of 1970, 850,000 professional nurses would be required, including 300,-000 with academic degrees. Viewing the situation more realistically, a goal of 680,000 was set. To accomplish this, it will be necessary to increase the rate of growth more than 20 per cent and also to provide the necessary numbers of teachers and supervisors.

Direct costs of hospital schools of nursing are fairly easy to determine. In many institutions, however, they represent only about a third of the total costs.

The following questions must be answered: Is it reasonable to expect students to pay their own way, or does the national need justify subsidies? What should be the criteria for supporting a student? Is federal support indicated or should the emphasis be on local or state aid? Which type of program is superior in terms of patient care and thereby deserving subsidy? Is it possible to reduce the costs of nursing education without sacrificing quality?

The full costs of "standby" facilities for local emergencies and indigent patients are seldom paid. Sentiment prevails that the community as a whole should assume responsibility for the full cost of caring for the hospitalized indigent. Such financial burden should not fall on the patient who pays his own hospital bill and Blue Cross premiums, or on the individual hospital.

Proper planning can control hospital costs. A long-term planning committee, set up by the individual hospital to define its functions and goals, can work closely with the

---

Service, Department of Health, Education and Welfare, Washington, D.C., February 1963.)

community planning agency to coordinate all health and hospital services whether under voluntary or government auspices and thereby assure the best health care always related to reasonable costs.

Such accomplishment cannot be expected overnight. It requires understanding the need for cooperative use of specialized equipment and services and also the elimination of unwarranted duplication.

PART TWO

The Hospital Team

4
What Trusteeship Involves

BOARD RESPONSIBILITIES

THE ORIGINAL CONCEPT OF A HOSPITAL was as a house of refuge conducted under church auspices and giving shelter to the wayfarer. Frequently it bore the title *Hôtel Dieu*.

Prompted by the same spirit of benevolence, other institutions soon developed, also financed by the church and certain wealthy citizens. Gradually hospital services were extended to larger population groups with ever growing health needs. In consequence the financial burden grew.

The hospital trustee assumes responsibility for the community health program. He is the director of its most important public utility. Today's trustee is a member of a group comprising representative citizens who volunteer their time and talents to formulate a comprehensive pattern of health care for their communities and to convince the community that the health package offered is efficient and comprehensive.

Hospital trusteeship is not to be confused with active management. In the conduct of his own affairs, the businessman not only delegates authority, but frequently is an active participant in organizational matters. But, as a hospital board member, his functions are confined to delegating authority, with no personal involvement other than to appoint the executive head. As a board member, he sets the pattern, furnishes the funds to provide the facilities, assures the presence of competent personnel, and reviews and appraises the results. He exerts pressure only in the event of dissatisfaction with the competence of the individual selected.

The professional aspects of hospital service constitute the most difficult area of trustee responsibility. As a layman, the trustee finds himself working in a field foreign to his background or training. As a result of this deficiency, he may hesitate to face the many issues involved. Through better orientation and understanding, he can gain a great sense of fulfillment.

A primary responsibility of the board member is to review the medical staff constitution and by-laws. This insures appointments and privileges that are in the best interests of patient care and that committee structure is adequate with every requirement listed by the Joint Commission on Accreditation of Hospitals maintained. If his institution fails to make the grade, he should investigate to see what is wrong.

To assure high standards of health care, the board member needs the cooperation of those individuals appointed by the board as service chiefs and practitioners.

This involves close working relationships with medical staff members in long-term planning and in maintaining high standards of patient care. Such relationships are promoted either through the admittance of one or more doctors to board membership—a debatable move—or by the presence of a strong joint conference committee, comprising an equal number of trustees and doctors. Irrespective of the technique, steps must be taken to develop closer coordination between administration and professional services.

Finance is a major concern of trustees. One recent study produced the fact that board members spend 40% of their time talking about finances; 20% on building improvement and equipment; 10% on nursing and patient care; 15% on medical staff issues; 10% on community relations and fund raising; and 5% on miscellaneous matters, including personnel.

It is the trustee's responsibility to make sure that the institution has sufficient funds to conduct its current and long-term planning programs, as well as to provide for the proper investment of unused funds. If he does not personally solicit financial support, he must initiate a suitable program. The budgeting process falls under the jurisdiction of the administration.

Constantly increasing costs of the necessary modern equipment and facilities focus attention upon budgets and financial statements. Expenses covering teaching and research programs must be met, based on the extent to which each hospital can afford to become involved in such areas. Important as finances are, board members should spend more time on patient care and medical staff matters.

The management pattern also must adjust to changing trends in the health field. The modern pattern comprises trustee responsibilities and functions, administrative methods, and medical staff attitudes and participation. Satisfied to sustain precepts acceptable 30 or more years ago, many trustees fail to appreciate that sound business judgment with increasing emphasis upon civic requirements overbalances emotional motivation in serving those unable to pay for treatment.

The broader areas of trustee obligation must be precisely defined. One hospital assigns its trustee responsibility to the following six categories: (1) purpose (this involves the extent of patient care, education, and research); (2) financial; (3) facilities and personnel; (4) professional; (5) public relations; and (6) quality of medical care.

Some pertinent questions concerning the trustee are: What are the hospital's five or ten year objectives? What yardsticks are available to measure the degree of progress? What provisions are made for a final evaluation?

The trustee is both morally and, to a certain degree, legally responsible for the proper care of patients. The standards for hospital accreditation as stipulated by the Joint Commision on Accreditation state that the governing board has the legal and moral responsibility for the conduct of the hospital as an institution. This board is responsible to the patient, to the community, and to the sponsoring organization. Thus, the trustee represents a corporation that is liable for negligent treatment on the part of physicians he appoints. He must also assume responsibility for the enforcement of such rules as may be deemed necessary for the safety of patients.

According to legal authorities, the chance of a trustee's being held liable for anything connected with the operation of the hospital is remote. In the event of injuries to patients, any liability incurred would be that of the corporation operating the hospital, or of the individual responsible. Because the administrator is the agent of the corporation and not of the board, the corporation would be responsible for his acts, as well as for the acts of other employees. The trustee would be personally responsible only if it were shown that he had participated actively in the negligence. Even under such circumstances he might be considered as agent of the corporation. He would be solely responsible if it were established that his act were unrelated to his functions as trustee.

Courts in an increasing number of jurisdictions have ruled that hospitals are responsible for the negligence of their employees. When negligence is attributable to the act of physicians or private duty nurses employed by the patient, the rulings are more specific on the basis that the hospital is not liable, because such individuals are responsible for their own acts as independent contractors.

A striking development in hospital management during the years has been an alteration in the status of the executive head. Many trustees used to contend that almost anyone can run a hospital. And almost anyone did. One board in the early 1890s advertised for "a man between the ages of 30 and 40, single, and of active and firm mind."

As these institutions advanced to more professional proportions, the matron or nurse superintendent became first choice among potential applicants. Because of her training, patient care was her major responsibility. In active partnership with those board members who had time and the inclination to become involved in business trivia, she fulfilled all administrative functions.

Going back only 20 years in the board minutes of one hospital, we find such revealing items as, "the superintendent discussed the purchase of a bookkeeping machine. Action was referred to a special committee of the board."; and, "the board considered the purchase of a new stoker for the boiler, which matter was referred to a friend, a local engineer." On another occasion the superintendent sought permission to purchase a watch clock for the night watchman.

Soon, a new type of management became essential. Hospital business demanded and began to receive the benefit of men and women holding advanced degrees in hospital and public health administration. As a result, the hospital administrator today assumes the same rank in community life as a bank president, a school head, or an industrial executive.

Selecting the right individual for the top executive post has become a major board responsibility. The appointee must be thoroughly qualified by training and experience, and he must have the proper personality. He must receive compensation adequate to his responsibilities, based on the size and type of hospital and community standards.

Graduate programs in hospital administration, sponsored by schools of public health or business administration now assure that there are sufficient numbers of men and women prepared to serve in the capacity of both the business executive and the professional counselor.

The trustee is a motivating factor in interpreting for the community the hospital's services and needs. He serves as contact man, prepared to present effectively the story of comprehensive health care, equipped to answer any questions concerning costs, and quick to squash damaging rumors that may be circulated.

The board member receives no financial benefit for his services, nor should he similarly benefit from any business transactions in which he may engage with the hospital. So strong is this feeling that certain states prohibit, by law, trustees of charitable institutions becoming involved in any hospital activity that would result in financial benefit to themselves. Where unselfish motivation can be proved the legality of such action would undoubtedly not be questioned. Nevertheless, to avoid any suspicion, the trustee would be better to remain free from such involvements.

Some hospitals make a practice of granting discounts in one form or another to employees, members of the medical staff and their families, trustees, also clergymen, policemen, and firemen, on the assumption that they are fringe benefits to individuals indirectly associated with the institution. Also, it is justifiable that the trustee be reimbursed for traveling expenses incurred when representing his hospital at conventions or meetings. Nevertheless, because of increasing public concern over hospital costs, and the stiffening attitude of government toward tax exemption, it is advisable to review such policies, and to avoid any practice that would threaten the hospital's charitable status.

A modern concept of board responsibilities is succinctly stated by Henry R. Stephenson, for many years a trustee of the Greenville General Hospital, Greenville, S. C., as follows:

The board should consider and approve the hospital's purpose and its yearly operating objectives. It should review and approve the hospital's long range objectives. These can be in the area of building, finances and special projects or programs. It should ask for and use yardsticks by which to measure progress toward the hospital's short range and long range objectives. It should review and approve the various budgets. These should include income, expense, cash flow, personnel and capital expenditures, budgets. These should be detailed and will allow for a more satisfying experience of planning and then review and finally appraisal.

The board should assure itself that the hospital staff is being developed to do a better job of caring for patients in the future and that it is being paid adequately. It should review the medical staff constitution and by-laws. It should be assured that appointments and privileges are consistent with each doctor's background and training. It should assure itself that the committee structure of the staff is functioning properly. It should concern itself with the quality of medical care as shown by clinical meetings of the staff to discuss deaths, complications, infections and difficult cases. It should insist that those things necessary to be done to be an accredited hospital, be done. Finally, it should review management's method and be assured that the best management tools are used.

WHO IS ELIGIBLE?

HOSPITAL BOARD MEMBERSHIP becomes an increasingly important function as the public more critically appraises the hospital management pattern. It brings into proper focus the board as planners, appraisers, and reviewers. It distinguishes those so serving as community leaders working on behalf of hospital interests in broader fields including legislation on a national, state, and local level. Because the hospital's reputation is measured by the competence, vision, and dedication of its policy makers, it is logical to expect that standards will apply eventually to this group paralleling those in professional areas under the Joint Commission on Accreditation of Hospitals.

The present need is for active participants who will contribute their time and talents to health work. Selection of board members is generally made on recommendation and action taken by the corporation where such a body exists, or by the governing board on a slate proposed by the nominating committee. It constitutes an important decision, for mistakes in appointment can have ramifications through the years.

A major factor in selectivity is the degree of talent the individual can contribute along with his sense of curiosity in exploring fields foreign to him. Other important considerations are his dedication to community welfare and his recognition of the hospital as a health center assuring a program based on current and long-term needs.

The board member must have the respect of the public

and recognition for his achievements in industry or his chosen profession. He must be sufficiently unselfish to give the time required to fulfill his obligations. Far more is required of modern-day stewardship than attendance at regular meetings. Extra hours are necessary on occasion, hours taken from work or from social and recreational activities. Generosity in contributing time is as important as financial contributions.

The trustee must be receptive to proper orientation and education in health affairs, humble in recognizing his limitations, willing to accept suggestions and criticisms. He may be forced to make embarrassing decisions which may jeopardize his personal relationships, and he must remain steadfast in his convictions under pressure.

Before hospital management attained "big business" rank, board members were selected for their ability to provide specialized skills which might benefit the institution. The lawyer was welcomed for his counsel on legal affairs, the newspaper publisher for his help in public relations, the banker for his investment advice, the building contractor for guidance in construction and renovation.

Granted the benefits of qualified opinion—and such benefits continue to be substantial—the pressures of modern hospital operation demonstrate the need for full-time staff specialists in certain areas. The certified public accountant becomes a full-time controller. Public relations responsibilities are frequently assigned to a director of development as part of the fund raising program. The value of the board member's presence is based on his performance as a member of a group faced with a myriad of problems.

Greater democracy is now evidenced in hospital board
appointments. Members should constitute a cross section
of the community, rather than a privileged minority. Because the hospital serves many whose costs must be met
by local government, representatives of tax spending
agencies may be eligible for the board. Educators and
members of the clergy have much to contribute. Labor
representatives may help greatly in solving personnel
problems of employees.

Considerable controversy has developed regarding the
presence of active medical staff members on hospital
boards. The pros and cons have been stated and restated
with the opposition in the majority. Principal objections
are:

embarrassment to the physician in being identified with
business operations; the possibility of being accused of acting
in behalf of selfish interests; suspicion developing over an individual being the appointee of the board rather than of his own
professional group.

Medical staff participation in hospital affairs can
better be accomplished through an active joint conference committee or its equivalent. Nevertheless, with
growing emphasis on the importance of the doctor as a
member of the hospital team, opposition to his participation in management and planning is diminishing. Instead it is being encouraged. He is becoming more closely
identified with the utilization of the hospital's resources
and more active in the administration of its professional
departments.

For many years hospital boards were essentially man's
domain. Notwithstanding the great contributions of

women in numerous areas, hospital business, it was felt, could better be conducted without feminine participation. Furthermore, it was argued, women with more time on their hands coupled with their unflagging zeal and extreme conscientiousness might be inclined to "take over."

World War II changed the situation. Women in vast numbers assumed responsibilities as volunteers and nurses aides that neither they nor anyone else believed were within their powers. These public spirited citizens knew hospitals from the inside out. They had proved their point.

Certain institutions designated as women's hospitals, children's hospitals, also others serving the chronically ill, were founded by women, and still remain under their control. The trend however is to supplement such boards with men who prove particularly helpful in offering financial and legal counsel.

Opposition to the presence of women as board members is rapidly disappearing. Sex, it is agreed, is not a determining factor in trustee appointments. Women are playing increasingly important roles as trustees and officers. One distinguished general hospital in the East attributes much of its progress to the leadership exercised by a woman president.

When the right woman is chosen she will serve faithfully and intelligently; when the wrong woman is selected she will present a problem. This also applies to men. The right choice depends upon proper screening and adequate preliminary investigation.

Using members of the same family on the hospital

board is debatable. If the board is to be truly representative of its community it is desirable to distribute responsibility, and thus assure complete coverage of local interests. Too many voluntary hospital boards have been too closely held when the presidency is handed down from one generation to another. In consequence such institutions have become inbred and are restricted in their philosophies and social planning.

Names alone mean little. Frequently board position has been sought and attained for its prestige value. Hopes to attract financial support through adding individuals of wealth and position have proved disappointing.

Little has been done to establish adequate standards for hospital board performance. Studies in this area would logically include productivity of services based on age spans. While the strength of many such groups lies in the maturity of their members, proper balance should be assured between younger participants and their seniors. Specifically, membership might well embrace a certain number of trustees under forty years, with others between forty and sixty, and some over sixty. The younger classification serves as insurance against the future and meets the need to provide continuity of planning. Such apportionment of age brackets can become difficult because of the heavier schedules carried by younger professionals and business executives. One junior executive when asked to serve on the hospital board, placed the matter before his superior officer. Was his organization willing to have him assume outside obligations which would involve additional demands upon his time and talents? He was encouraged to serve since he would be rendering important community service.

Early retirement of business executives and others from professional ranks promises mixed blessings. It can mean greater support from lay groups. It can also present threats to hospital management. The hospital president or other officer relieved from the pressures of active careers and ready to give their "all" to their institutions can literally "take over." Assurance of security in the form of a desk or an office may tempt them to become involved in management. On the other hand, the services awaiting them as community leaders in health affairs can prove both stimulating and productive.

Our hospitals have a great need of a substantial army of public spirited citizens which, by the soundness of its knowledge and the strength of its opinion, will determine the type of health and hospital care the American public wants and needs. Such leadership can develop best through competent hospital stewardship.

IMPORTANCE OF ORIENTATION

MANY A PROMISING NEWCOMER TO THE HOSPITAL board has failed to live up to what the group expected of him through lack of adequate orientation. In the hope of gaining his acceptance, the responsibilities of hospital stewardship are treated casually or completely overlooked. Too late the new incumbent discovers what he has let himself in for.

Before accepting an invitation to participate, the prospective board member should know the responsibilities he is to assume. To avoid later misunderstandings, he should be invited to sit in on a board meeting to follow the procedures and to observe members in action. As superficial as such an experience may be, it will convince him that the job is not a simple one and that it may be months before he can participate intelligently.

Too often the hospital trustee is the forgotten man in the hospital's education program. Courses are available to those who would become administrators and much stress is laid upon the training of physicians, nurses, and other professionals. Yet those who are responsible for policies and over-all planning receive scant attention other than sporadic invitations to participate in "institutes" or "workshops" which are more frequently refused than accepted.

Adequate orientation for new board members serves a three-fold purpose: it assures the administrator of more competent support; it allows the work to assume far greater meaning for the board member; and it strengthens the management pattern.

The problem that remains to be solved is how basic comprehension of hospital and community health services can be accomplished. As busy individuals with many personal interests and obligations, trustees cannot be expected to make great sacrifices of time and effort. Yet it is essential they have some knowledge.

Because of his professional background, the administrator logically sets the pattern for his board members. Formerly, certain less confident executives were reluctant to involve their trustees in hospital affairs. Today, hospital administrators are generally better prepared for their executive responsibilities.

In orienting and assuring the continued education of the new trustee, the administrator may well be aided by some officer or other knowledgeable board member. From personal experience such individuals will be able to provide most effectively the information a board member needs. To assure more complete concepts of modern health care, it has been suggested that future trustees receive at least 30 hours of orientation training, provided under the auspices of local and regional planning councils, hospitals in the area, the county medical society, and universities offering programs of hospital administration.

The trustee's most important function, and one in which he frequently is least prepared, is his responsibility to provide high standards of professional care. Because he appoints physicians to the medical staff, he should know how to judge their qualifications, also what constitutes staff privileges. He should familiarize himself with medical staff bylaws, and recognize the relationship between the governing board and the professional staff. He should have a clear understanding of professional standards as established by the Joint Commission on Accreditation of Hospitals, and he must be aware of his obligation to assure high-quality patient care.

New concepts of patient care deserve the trustee's attention, including the importance of the recovery room, the potentials of progressive care, changes in the functions of the emergency department. He needs to be made aware of the importance of the home care program, or its equivalent, as one device which will help reduce over-utilization of hospital beds.

No better opportunity for becoming familiar with the professional aspects of the hospital can be provided the trustee than sitting in on meetings of the joint conference committee. Here he learns of medical needs and policies. Furthermore, acquaintance with professional achievements will enable him to talk with greater conviction on health and hospital affairs.

The trustee should be made conscious of his own legal responsibilities. He will want to study the financial budget as well as the hospital's rate structure. He should be brought up to date on the hospital's programs in education and research. He should have a clear understanding of the role of the auxiliary, its function and organization including the contributions made by in-service volunteers. If there is a master plan for future growth and development he will want to study it. If no such plan exists he might well institute one.

One trustee offers the following suggestion:

Give us first an overall picture of the hospital's major procedures, its weaknesses as well as its strengths. It's a strange world to most of us, and we need to develop a sense of belonging, to feel we are really a part of the institution.

Because of the importance of his appointment the new member should be properly introduced to his board associates, to the chief of medical staff, and other department heads. News releases should be dispatched to the local press.

Suggested reading may well include a copy of the con-

stitution and bylaws of the institution and its medical
staff, and some historical review of the hospital's background will prove informative. Close study of the organization chart will focus attention upon interdepartmental
relationships and also indicate the points of authority.

For a broader understanding of hospital and health
needs there is "Trustee," the pocket-sized magazine published monthly by the American Hospital Association in
the interests of better stewardship. Occasional articles
appearing in professional journals likewise should be
called to his attention.

A tour of the building and properties is an essential part
of the orientation program. Unfortunately such inspection
is too often superficial. Each department deserves its
share of attention not only for its own specific functions,
but also for its relationship to other services in meeting
the needs of the sick.

The trustee's attendance and participation in institutes
or workshops held under the auspices of universities and
hospital associations should be encouraged. One such
course covers the following major topics—the purpose,
function, and structure of hospital boards; the trustee's
relationship with the medical staff including structure of
the medical staff and its committees; the role of the physician in private practice and the hospital setting; hospital
law, including legal responsibilities to the patient, personnel, and medical staff; and finally the trustee's relationship with the hospital administration.

Participation in local hospital or health councils will
enable the trustee to speak with greater authority on

mutual problems, procedures, and objectives. Most revealing to him would be a day or two spent at the annual convention of the American Hospital Association.

If the orientation program is successful it will convince the newcomer that there is a job to be done and that he has something to contribute to it. He will accept the fact that the same principles of management he observes in the conduct of his own enterprise apply equally to hospitals. Numerous instances can be recounted where on entering the hospital board room a successful business leader violates rules he would stoutly uphold in his own domain.

The follow-through of the orientation program frequently constitutes some specific committee assignment in an area in which the appointee has had previous experience. A broader view of trustee responsibilities is possible through a rotating plan of committee involvement, particularly participation in meetings of the joint conference committee or its equivalent.

The board meeting may profitably include some educational feature. This may be a description of a hospital department by its head, a brief talk on new trends in hospital and health care by a guest speaker, or open discussion on pending legislation affecting hospital services. Motion pictures, such as the film "A Position of Trust" distributed by the American Hospital Association, are available and can be enlightening and stimulating to lay groups.

Unfortunately, too frequently the trustee gets only the bad news—financial problems, tragic situations, violations of established rules and regulations by doctors and others. Seldom does he hear the good things. Success stories are welcome and stimulating on board meeting agendas— accounts by doctors and surgeons of interesting cases of recovery due to professional skill and scientific equipment.

One trustee group was particularly fortunate in hearing a first hand success story. The patient in question, a man of middle age, had been discharged following recovery from surgery to replace a useless heart valve. According to the doctor's report—"eight months were required to build up the patient's physical condition before the surgery could be undertaken." To which the administrator added—"and it took virtually all the staff and a total of sixteen months to do the trick, that, and $8,000 worth of free care."

Similar examples of the triumph of life over death are written in the records of every modern hospital. No better answers can be found to the question of why hospital costs are high.

Hospital tours should be continued in the program of education. Hospital visits should take place frequently to keep the board member up-to-date on changes in departmental services, new equipment, and advances in patient care. With accompanying explanations by the administrator, a medical staff member, or both, he will learn about the strengths and weaknesses of his institution.

A news letter or its equivalent is of great help to the trustee in supplying such essential facts as occupancy figures, numbers of admissions and discharges, as well as certain observations on the institution's financial position.

It should not be the purpose of a comprehensive program of education to promote the hospital board member to professional rank. He should serve solely as a public-spirited citizen concerned with community health standards, sufficiently informed to interpret what those standards should be, and ready to take any necessary action to maintain them.

Over-exposure to hospital routine can precipitate embarrassing situations leading to an image of what hospital people point to as the "meddling trustee." Such an individual is encountered most frequently in smaller communities where relationships are closer. With time on his hands, he drops in at the hospital unannounced, wanders about, chatting with this or that employee to get an idea of "what's going on." Under such circumstances the administrator should point to the inviolable rule "no visiting unaccompanied by some representative of management."

Proper orientation along with continued education for board members is essential within certain limitations. Over stimulation can, on the other hand, tangle the lines of authority.

No type of management can survive two bosses and hospitals are no exception. It is important that the hospital trustee understand his position as separate from that of the executive officer.

EVALUATING MEDICAL CARE

EVALUATING MEDICAL CARE does not necessarily
imply interference. It becomes a most important function,
calling for courage, sound counsel, and full cooperation
on the part of all concerned. There must be mutual recognition of community health needs.

The incongruity of legal and moral responsibility for
patient welfare invested in a lay group, frequently with
little or no background on which to appraise the quality
of medical care, is immediately apparent. This does not
lessen the obligation of the trustee to insist on high standards of professional care. Bylaws should be studied and
reviewed at frequent intervals assuring the board complete control, with the right to limit, suspend, or termi-
nate staff privileges, or to grant additional privileges as
may seem warranted.

Selection of the medical staff is the first step in assuring
high standards of professional care. Medical staff appointment is a privilege, not a right. Whereas the trustee must
depend upon his administrator and medical board to
evaluate applicants, he should be sufficiently conversant
with the requirements to assure himself that he is voting
intelligently. The board of a voluntary hospital can ex-
clude any doctors who, in its opinion, are undesirable or
unqualified, from staff membership or from treating patients in the hospital.

Foremost among the criteria for evaluating the applicant is his standing in his professional societies. The first

attempt to establish standards and professional requirements was the founding of the American College of Surgeons in 1913 and the American College of Physicians in
1915.

Fellowship in the American College of Surgeons requires seven years experience, following graduation from
medical school, and includes two to four years of post-
graduate training. Final approval rests with a State and
National Credentials Committee.

Fellowship in the American College of Physicians requires high standing in internal medicine and cardiology,
gastro-enterology, dermatology, pediatrics, psychiatry,
neurology, pathology, radiology, or public health. This
means a year of internship and three years of graduate
training, with some concentration of professional activity.

The first board of certification of specialists was formed
in 1917. Nineteen such boards are now recognized by the
Council on Medical Education and Hospitals of the American Medical Association, each of which is responsible for
certification in its individual specialty. Basic qualifications for certification include graduation from an approved medical school, one year's internship, three to five
years of approved post-graduate training, with rigid written and practical examinations.

Before taking final action in staff appointments, the
trustee can seek counsel from members of the credentials
committee, the joint conference committee, or others who
may have authority. Should the applicant lack professional certification, there must be an equivalent of train-

ing and experience. References may be solicited from the dean of the medical college from which he graduated.

In the opinion of many, every ethical, licensed physician in a community should be permitted to serve on the staff of its hospital provided he agrees to abide by the medical staff bylaws and does not violate that agreement. Because some physicians are not as well qualified as others, it is important to specify the privileges accorded each member of the staff and to limit those privileges to the services his education and experience permit him to render.

Answers to the following questions should be considered before appointments are made: What was the applicant's record in those hospitals where he served his internship and residency? What was his reputation in other institutions with which he may have been identified? What contribution has he made to scientific literature? What and how many papers has he written and had published? Does he attend national scientific meetings and on what programs has he appeared? How active is he in local, state, or national professional groups?

Satisfied that he has provided the hospital with a qualified staff, the trustee faces another important obligation. How can he hope to estimate good medical practice?

The medical or staff audit is the most scientific method of measuring hospital care. It provides a basis for appraising the professional work of the institution as well as the services rendered by each individual. Medical records comprise the "books" of the staff audit. These are studied with particular attention to comparisons of risks on admission and discharge, use made of consultation services, and comparisons of surgical diagnosis with tissue findings of the pathologist. Through such studies the trustee is acquainted with the mortality and infection rates, also the morbidity results, percentage of successes, and the partial successes and failures of each staff member. In addition he is better able to grade staff members for promotion or seniority.

Staff audits may be conducted by the group itself, by a professional statistician or other qualified, unbiased individual. The final report is referred to the administrator who submits it to the staff and the governing board for any necessary action.

The medical records room is in reality the conscience of the hospital. Adequate records are essential to efficient hospital organization. They contribute to proper patient care and frequently play an important part in legal proceedings. They are generally conceded to be the property of the hospital, and not of the patient or the doctor. Unless proved mentally incompetent the patient has the legal right to examine his record. Under certain conditions hospital records are admissible in the evidence of the courts of litigation. However, no records should be released, except on subpoena, without written consent of the patient.

Failure to complete records places a strain upon hospital relationships. Because of pressing demands upon their time, staff members are tempted to procrastinate. In the event that disciplinary efforts of the medical staff are ineffectual, it may be necessary for the board of governors to become involved. Actually all records should be maintained day by day.

Percentage of autopsies is another important gauge by which the trustee can measure professional accomplishment. The morgue can and should be a classroom for the most important teaching the hospital can provide.

Autopsy figures are not to be lightly dismissed. A comparatively low percentage of post-mortems can be indicative of disinterest. At 20 per cent or below, there is danger of the hospital losing its accreditation. Some institutions show figures as high as 70 per cent or more. Logical questions the layman may well raise are: To what extent are doctors striving to gain permission to perform autopsies? and What is the administration doing to cooperate?

Surgical removal of more than 12 per cent to 15 per cent normal tissue as in appendectomies, for example, bears investigation. This is commonly the responsibility of a tissue committee.

Number of consultations can be indicative of the interest evinced by individual staff members to seek additional professional opinion.

The death rate is another valuable gauge. According to studies made, the post-operative death rate for surgical patients during the first ten days after surgery should not run much over one per cent. More than 0.25 per cent of one per cent for maternity cases is debatable, as is also an infant mortality of more than 2 per cent during the first ten days. Caesarean sections, post-operative infections, and post-anesthesia complications need similarly to be watched.

Fee splitting, that unethical procedure dramatically portrayed in national periodicals, may well exist without the trustee's knowledge, but this does not absolve him from responsibility.

Definite problems must be recognized in the board's appraisal of medical care. Close personal relations between the staff member and the trustee he serves professionally can become a deterrent to unbiased judgment. The busy board member, already overburdened with personal affairs, is reluctant to exert judgment on matters with which he is unfamiliar. Furthermore, physicians are not always inclined to share professional knowledge with lay groups.

In contrast to the disposition of many board members to refrain from a too intimate involvement in medical matters, there are the few who let their enthusiasm get the better of them and confuse evaluation with interference.

The answer to these problems is found in a medical staff willing to realize its responsibilities to the patient, also the position of trust assumed by the board, with the administrator serving as coordinator. The medical staff must establish the yardsticks for evaluation. Through its regular progress reports, both trustees and staff members are kept informed on professional performance. Only by close teamwork can accurate evaluation be assured.

CAPITAL FUNDS AND FINANCING

THE NATION's total investment in hospital resources now stands at approximately thirteen billion dollars. This is almost four times the investment of thirty
years ago. Financing these institutions constitutes big
business.

At present the hospital's principal sources of capital
funds are government, operating surpluses, contributions
from the hospital group, and general philanthropy.

Two facts stand out in hospital financing. First, government is an increasingly important source of capital funds.
Second, such funds will be used to provide and to preserve
modern hospital facilities for the entire community, following the pattern of coordinated health and hospital
services. Federal and state government both are greater
factors in the coverage of the hospital expenses of medical
indigents.

The Hill–Burton legislation was regarded with suspicion by hospital administration when first enacted in
1946. It was originally labeled the "Hospital Survey and
Construction Act", or "Public Law 725." According to the
requirements, the government matched funds for construction purposes on a one-two basis with state and local
funds. Managing the federal government's participation in
the program is the surgeon general of the United States
Public Health Service who works with a federal hospital
council of eight members, four of whom are technical experts in hospital and medical care. Experience has proven

the potentialities of government aid properly controlled and operating in conjunction with hospital groups on a state and local level. This act reveals hospital service as an ancillary activity of the government, rather than a primary service.

A five-year extension to the Hill–Burton Act marks the fourth time that Congress has revised the hospital construction program. Federal spending authority is now raised to over $300,000,000 annually. For one year this included $140,000,000 specifically for new hospital construction, $20,000,000 for special modernization projects, $70,000,000 for construction of long-term care facilities, and $10,000,000 for construction of rehabilitation facilities.

Originally no provision was made for modernization. The law specified that priority be given "hospitals serving rural communities and areas with relatively small financial resources." In consequence urban hospital projects seldom benefited. Now a separate modernization program gives priority to projects in densely populated districts.

The balance of capital funds other than operating income is derived from contributions from the hospital's "inner circle" and general philanthropy. Contributions from within the hospital group reflect the original concept of trusteeship—a philanthropist who responds generously to the needs of his institution. The board member of today, burdened by increasing taxes, is less apt to personally supply major financial support.

The extent to which medical staff members should support hospital fund raising efforts reflects individual attitudes. Some professional fund raisers place the doctors' obligation at ten per cent of the hospital's capital requirements. Valuable as the doctor's support is, the question remains whether this should not be based upon his position as a member of the community, rather than his place as a member of the staff.

General philanthropy includes donations from corporations, community fund drives, grants from foundations, and bequests. To an increasing extent, appeals have placed emphasis upon corporation support on behalf of the community hospital. To substantiate such claims, formulas are employed based on the utilization of the hospital's services by company employees. Hope of attaining the established goal rests in the allegiance of the corporate giver. Whether such allegiance will continue on the basis of formulas based on a single unit or on long-range planning remains to be seen.

Contributions to hospitals constitute one of the most important categories of corporate giving. Close to a quarter of a billion dollars come each year from such sources. This relationship has encouraged greater numbers of business executives to participate as members of hospital boards.

Such affiliation helps to supply the answers to pertinent questions such as: Why do hospitals operate at a ratio of from two to two and a half employees per patient? What is being done to control these figures through automation or labor saving devices? Are hospital accounting systems as efficient as they should be? On what basis are hospitals adding to their bed capacities?

Foundations have long been the hope and the despair of hospital fund raisers. These agencies hesitate to contribute to bricks and mortar, at least on the basis of the inadequate proof of need as is often presented. Nor is there much encouragement from the general public because of the growing concern over the effectiveness of our hospital system. Foundations demand evidence of basic research that will blaze new trails in medical science or raise the standards of hospital management. Unfortunately many applications for grants are unconvincing, and show little attempt to coincide with each foundation's particular areas of interest and support.

In the past, a substantial portion of the hospital's financial aid has been allocated to acute bed facilities and accompanying services. Looking ahead, boards of trustees, administration, and medical staff members recognize that the use of such funds must be predicated on carefully formulated programs to reduce bed expansion and to place greater emphasis upon the needs for nursing homes, chronic and mental facilities, rehabilitation centers, outpatient departments, and home-care programs. More conspicuously featured in development programs are the replacement and modernization of buildings long since outdated.

Two approaches are possible in soliciting hospital support: the long-term development program and the short, intensive fund raising campaign. Frequently fund raising becomes part of the broader concepts of developing public interest in hospital affairs.

The long-term approach is gaining importance due to a

growing acceptance of the fact that hospitals need friends. It is furthermore obvious that lasting and understanding friendship cannot be accomplished through short, spasmodic efforts. The value of preliminary communication, with consistent follow-through is now recognized. Community understanding and support comes only through appreciation of the services rendered and for this the public must have the facts.

Before any efforts are made in this direction, a sympathetic environment must be created by the hospital group and substantial funds should be available to ensure the program a good start. Following this comes the appointment of a leader. The potential candidate must be compatible with the community. Experience in public relations or affiliated areas, with some native background are assets. Otherwise, he must possess the ability to adapt himself to local and regional characteristics. The success of the individual's efforts will depend in large measure upon the support he receives from the hospital group, and particularly upon its acceptance of the fact that results do not come over night. A year or more may be required before any fair evaluation of the program can be made.

The long-term development program can be as extensive or as simple as best fits the hospital pattern. Its proper functions include directing bequests to the institution through contacts with attorneys, bankers, trust officers, members of the clergy, investment brokers, and physicians. More routine procedures require preparation and distribution of hospital literature reflecting regional and national aspects of health care, utilization of radio and television facilities, maintaining contact with the press, and personal appearances before civic, fraternal, and religious groups.

The short-term, intensive fund raising program, long successful in meeting the requirements of the individual hospital, is now being applied with good results to regional needs. Under professional leadership many more hospitals are demonstrating the benefits of common endeavor to provide health and hospital facilities on an area-wide basis.

The short-term program may serve effectively in conjunction with the long-term program. In such capacity it benefits from the presence of a well enlightened public, prepared to accept statements of need with many questions already answered. The hospital trustee guided by his administrator must determine the best approach, selecting the professional counsel that will work most successfully with the hospital team.

The term "fund raiser" is misleading and a more precise term is "fund raising counselor." This differentiation is not always made clear to members of the hospital group who imagine such an individual waving a magic wand that releases the community's bank roll.

The fund raising counselor's first task is to estimate the maximum sum possible within certain time limits. Assured on this point he investigates sources of competent leadership. Such responsibility may rest in the hands of one individual or constitute a partnership. Among essential qualifications are vision, interest, conviction of need, personality, diplomacy, and determination.

Once the leader is appointed the mechanism of the program begins to take form. The professional counselor proceeds to assemble the various elements and available talents, coaches the participants, assists in the preparation and the distribution of printed matter, and develops a routine for auditing and verifying gifts and pledges.

Close cooperation between fund raising counsel and hospital administration is important. For this reason, care should be exercised in selecting an agency whose representatives are of the type and character to fit happily into the hospital and community background. The administrator serves as collaborator with the fund raising counselor, but never as an active solicitor.

The American Association of Fund Raising Counsel comprises some 30 fund raising firms scattered across the country whose clients include nearly 90 per cent of the professionally managed fund programs using outside counsel. Under its Fair Practice Code, business is done only on the basis of a specified fee, determined before the program begins. There is no percentage or commission on the sums raised. Furthermore, the executive head of the member organization must have at least a six-year record of continuous experience as a professional in fund raising. Further assurance of procuring qualified counsel is the list of professional fund raisers compiled by the American Hospital Association.

Estimates show that a professional campaign can be conducted at a cost of under six per cent of the total collections. This includes professional fees and other expenses for printing, mailing, etc.

More conservative members of the hospital group may question the justification of paying outsiders for services that in their opinion can as well be rendered from within. Fund raising, they will soon discover, is a business in its own right. Experienced fund raising counsel is worth its cost, if for no other reason than providing moral support through its knowledge of how and when to extract money from a frequently reluctant public. The push and direction that outsiders can provide cannot be duplicated from within.

Capital expenditures are not to be confused with current expenditures. Capital needs apply to construction and modernization. Current expenditures involve payment for patient care, including the problem of the average individual's ability to meet the costs of necessary professional care.

Health insurance coverage through Blue Cross, which covers hospital care exclusively, and Blue Shield, which provides medical and surgical care, along with commercial plans have had a marked effect on the utilization of hospitals. According to recent figures approximately one hundred and forty million persons receive benefits from various types of health insurance.

Recent figures of the United States Department of Labor reveal that employers' contributions for the purchase of health insurance for employees and dependents amounted to over three billion dollars, much of which goes to the support of hospitals. Such benefits place demands upon hospital management to provide proof of operating under sound business principles.

Commercial insurance, while unquestionably a factor in the national picture, does not constitute a social program. In contrast to the nonprofit plans, it offers cash payments for specified contingencies in lieu of providing for services.

Blue Cross, in particular, has contributed greatly to the rapid growth and the expansion of hospital and health care in this country. It has, in effect, helped preserve the original concept of voluntary support. It originated in Dallas, Texas, in 1929, where Baylor University Hospital was having financial problems. In consequence the top officials of the hospital and university decided to experiment by enrolling groups of public subscribers for hospital care on a prepayment basis. Because the idea fulfilled a need among the teaching staff of the University, that particular segment of the population constituted the first group to sign up. Soon other workers in banks, oil companies, and various occupations followed. Originally Blue Cross membership was confined principally to group enrollment. Sensing the need for expanding this principle, its privileges were extended to include individuals within certain limitations.

Since the inception of voluntary health insurance plans, large labor unions have gained recognition for prepaid health coverage for their members. These take various forms, such as that which insures the workers through a welfare fund directed by a board comprising both labor and management. Under this arrangement, employees are covered by both Blue Cross and Blue Shield, with premiums paid by the fund. Other unions operate and control hospitals whose services are available only to members. In such instances, the doctors are employed directly by the union. Sometimes the union contracts directly with the hospitals and doctors.

Numerous independent health plans have been developed to meet local needs. Originally all medical group-practice units operating under prepayment plans were sponsored by industrial plants, farm groups, or labor unions. Later, physicians started their own units. Community enterprises also have developed following the pattern of the Health Insurance Plan of Greater New York.

While they are not intended as a solution to the over-all medical problems of the country, the value of such independent services has been demonstrated by their increasing enrollment.

5

Professional Organization

MEDICAL STAFF RULES AND BYLAWS

THE PROFESSIONAL structure of our hospitals—
the rules and bylaws under which they operate—is determined by the size of the institution and the nature of
its services.

The present trend is to include matters pertaining to
the appointment, duties, and responsibilities of the staff
both in the bylaws of the governing board and in the
bylaws of the medical staff organization. This practice is
based on the premise that the governing board is responsible for the quality of the medical care given patients,
and therefore has the duty and responsibility of appointing the staff and of making reasonable regulations for the
control of the medical work of the hospital. This is solely
to insure the allocation of control where it rightfully
belongs with the governing board.

Self-government has characterized the medical staff
organization and has proved successful where effectively
applied. Unfortunately controls are not always rigidly

observed in this structure. Many such failures may be traced to poorly conceived and executed bylaws, a situation that can be corrected by following a pattern such as that developed by the Joint Commission on Accreditation of Hospitals.

An organization chart clearly defined and up to date in formulating rules and regulations for new health services is essential. According to standards developed by the American Medical Association and the American College of Surgeons the line of authority stems from the board of directors down to the administrator and from the joint conference committee or its equivalent to the medical staff.

In some hospitals, principally those of 250 and more beds, a medical director heads the staff, constituting a role with many variations. Under favorable circumstances he relieves the board of certain responsibilities. His duties are not to be confused with those of the administrator, who exerts no direct control over the medical staff. Actually, this individual is a member of the administration concerned with the proper organization of the medical staff and seeing that it performs its requisite functions. While usually responsible for radiology, laboratories, pharmacy, and medical records, his primary interest is medical staff affairs as well as providing channels of communication between the medical staff, the governing board, and the administration.

In smaller institutions the chief of staff, who may also be president of the staff, fulfills much the same function. Irrespective of his title, he sets the framework for high

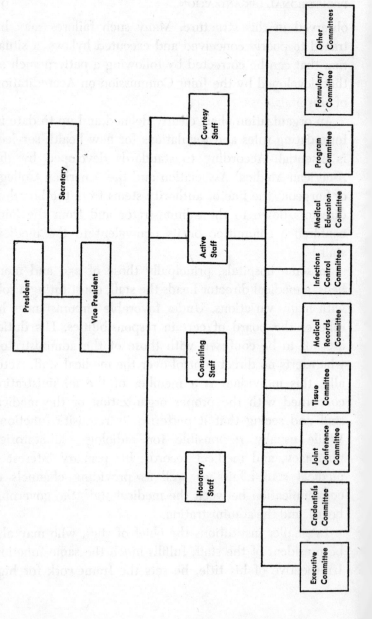

CHART II. ORGANIZATION OF MEDICAL STAFF FOR AVERAGE-SIZED HOSPITAL

President

Secretary

Vice President

Honorary Staff

Consulting Staff

Active Staff

Courtesy Staff

Executive Committee

Credentials Committee

Joint Conference Committee

Tissue Committee

Medical Records Committee

Infections Control Committee

Medical Education Committee

Program Committee

Formulary Committee

Other Committees

quality care and medical staff cooperation. Appointment should be made by the board of trustees on recommendation of the medical staff.

Numerous factors need to be considered in developing an organizational structure for the medical staff. What has long perplexed the American public, and even some hospital trustees, is why the patient cannot be treated at the hospital of his own choice. He can only if his doctor is a member of the staff of that institution, has courtesy privileges, or can gain them. Otherwise he must settle for accomodations in the hospital where his doctor has the privilege to send him—unless he feels so strongly that he transfers his care to someone on the staff of the hospital of his choice. The answer to this problem rests upon whether the particular institution operates with a so-called "open," or a "closed" staff. An open staff permits any licensed doctor to use the hospital's facilities, provided he adheres to the rules and regulations established. He has no staff appointment and no agreement with the hospital. The closed staff offers no courtesy privileges. This can contribute to an "inbred," autocratic attitude, making it difficult to open the doors to newcomers. Under such conditions the board must use its prerogative of exercising jurisdiction over the staff.

Most voluntary hospitals today have "open-controlled" staffs. These are active or attending staffs that take care of ward or service cases in addition to private cases. There is also a courtesy staff which has the privilege of serving private patients only. All members of the attending and courtesy staffs are appointed by the governing board and must sign an agreement to abide by the bylaws, rules, and regulations.

A registered hospital, one that meets all requirements set by the Joint Commission on Accreditation of Hospitals, admits only those doctors who are graduates of accredited medical schools and who are eligible for membership in their local medical societies. In consequence they automatically bar others which in itself constitutes limitations.

The type of staff organization decided upon must rest with the hospital and the community. Institutions with teaching affiliations which assume responsibility for educating interns and residents, will find their needs best served by closed or restricted staffs. Here teaching abilities in addition to proficiency in providing patient care require greater selectivity in appointments.

Two major groups appear in the hospital organizational pattern. The active attending staff speaks and acts with authority and guides the governing board in professional affairs. Other members enjoy honorary, consulting, or courtesy privileges. The consulting group is a senior body of recognized specialists in their respective fields, members or "fellows" of national organizations representing their specialties, or advisers to those having less training or experience. Appointment is made upon action by the governing board either through promotion from the active staff or by invitation. Consultants have no vote and hold no executive office. Their presence at staff meetings, while desirable, is purely voluntary.

Physicians who desire the use of hospital facilities for private patients but do not participate in the general activities of the institution are accorded courtesy rank. Such privilege is confined to those hospitals operating under the open-controlled staff pattern. Courtesy staff members are assigned no duties, but are charged with maintaining standards and adhering to all rules and regulations. They can attend staff meetings at will, but have no right to vote or hold office. Appointment is made by the governing board on recommendation by the medical staff.

The generally accepted form of organization for the medical staff is by clinical departments with a department for each specialty, the number varying with the size of the institution and the scope of its program. Clinical departments in the larger hospitals commonly include medicine, surgery, obstetrics, orthopedics, gynecology, pediatrics, urology, ophthalmology, otorhinolarynology, neurology, psychiatry and dermatology. General practitioners are assigned to the various clinical services in accordance with their qualifications. Their organization is chiefly administrative.

To each clinical department a head is appointed by the board. To an increasing extent these individuals are employed on a salaried full-time basis. This follows the trend of employing increasing numbers of professional personnel in hospitals.

Rules and bylaws should be specific and clearly stated. They must conform to local, state, and federal laws. In public hospitals these may be regulated by statute.

Whether it is a question of new bylaws or merely recasting those already in use, the assistance of competent legal counsel is important.

Basically, typical bylaws and rules and regulations serve the same purpose. Bylaws set forth the fundamental principles, outline the general organization, and establish standards for the overall conduct of all those involved. Rules and regulations define the mechanics by which the standards of service are met. In consequence, they offer greater flexibility in making changes necessary to keep pace with new developments.

Bylaws are generally prepared by a committee appointed for that particular purpose, after which they are reviewed by the medical staff. The staff's recommendations are then forwarded to the governing board for appraisal and final adoption.

The essentials of good bylaws and regulations include:

(1) An outline of organization including ethics, purposes, and minimum qualifications for membership.

(2) Procedures for granting and rescinding privileges.

(3) Terms of appointment of staff members and chiefs of clinical services including age of retirement from active service.

(4) Importance of maintaining up-to-date medical records. This constitutes an obligation of the trustees since proper clinical records are an important adjunct to good medical care.

(5) Schedule of regular monthly staff meetings with suitable programs and attendance requirements.

The Joint Commission on Accreditation of Hospitals

requires that "the hospital staff shall conduct a regular monthly staff conference to review the work of the various departments, to study interesting cases and select autopsy records for general discussion."

The American College of Surgeons likewise stipulates that "staff meetings be held at least once a month." According to the model bylaws of the American Hospital Association at least one hour of the monthly meeting must be allotted to clinical conferences. Some bylaws require automatic termination of the membership of a staff physician who without reasonable justification fails to attend three consecutive meetings.

Definition of types of patients to be treated, with authority of the administrator to govern admissions is commonly incorporated in modern bylaws; also some statement concerning requirements for consultation is often included.

The trustee is frequently at a disadvantage when making staff appointments. How can he as a layman appraise the professional skills of the doctor or surgeon? Obviously he must depend upon his administrator and medical board to examine all applicants. At the same time he should be sufficiently conversant with the requirements to satisfy himself that he is voting intelligently.

Application for membership is usually submitted to the administrator. Either he or the credentials committee of the medical staff verifies the information it contains. From there it goes to the executive committee of the medical staff with recommendations for appointment and privileges to be granted, or no appointment. Next it receives the attention of the attending staff, the joint conference committee, and finally the governing board. Generally the governing board corroborates the decisions reached. If not, additional information may be requested.

During the period that intervenes before final approval the board member has an opportunity to seek counsel from various sources. These may include members of the credentials or joint conference committee, the administrator, or others able to speak with some authority. Such independent investigation will reassure him that he is acting in the best interests of the hospital.

The most obvious source for evaluating the rating of the staff applicant is his standing in his professional societies. Membership in such professional organizations as the American College of Surgeons, American College of Physicians, or the American Academy of Pediatrics, or standing as a diplomate of an American specialty board gives evidence of the physician's professional standing.

The hospital board needs to supply no reason for rejecting the application of any physician for staff membership. Since it is responsible for the standards of medical care in the institution, it can refuse admission to anyone who, in its best judgment, fails to qualify. Many hospitals, however, do supply cause for their action.

The chief of staff's position is frequently the most difficult to fill. This is partly due to the absence of any specific definition of what the job comprises. Such appointments should not be based on any popularity contest nor should they be granted as a reward for faithful service.

The individual selected should be the keystone to good

organization. He must possess the attributes of true leadership—the ability to make decisions yet not become a dictator, to understand people and work well with them, and to communicate successfully. Most important, he must have the time or be willing to make the necessary time to fulfill the responsibilities he assumes.

One method of appointment is to have the medical staff nominate two or three individuals from which the governing board selects one. The principal duty of the chief of staff is to maintain the highest possible quality of medical care through careful supervision of the clinical work.

Appointments of staff members are generally for terms of one year. This assures flexibility in handling instances of unsatisfactory performance without the necessity of bringing charges against the individual. Should the terms of officers, the chief of staff, or chiefs of service be longer —that is, for two or three years—it would be well to indicate clearly that those terms are subject to annual appointment.

The delicate problem of retirement is a matter for each hospital medical staff and governing board to decide. Experience has shown the hazards of attempting to establish a specific age at which any individual becomes ineffective. Nevertheless, the Joint Commission on Accreditation of Hospitals, asserts that all medical staff bylaws, rules, and regulations should include a definite policy in this matter. Statistics indicate that 80 per cent of all accredited hospitals have a mandatory retirement age for the active staff of 65 years; about 5 per cent use the ages of 60 or 62, and about 15 per cent the ages of 68 to 70. This last age bracket is found most frequently in the large teaching or university hospitals. On retirement, appointment to the honorary or consulting staff may be granted.

COMMITTEES AND THEIR FUNCTIONS

THE AMERICAN HOSPITAL Association's "Model Constitution and By-Laws" calls for the following committees of the medical staff—executive, joint conference, credentials, medical records and tissue. These are likewise required by the Joint Commission on Accreditation of Hospitals. Also, occasionally included, are an infection controls committee, utilization committee, medical education committee or others as required to meet changing needs. Sometimes in the smaller institutions there is merely an executive committee or responsibility may be invested in the medical staff as a whole.

The executive committee is the governing group, determining policies for the medical staff, and providing surveillance and counseling of its members to assure high standards of patient care. It reviews reports of the five essential committees and takes disciplinary action when necessary. In conjunction with a competent chief of staff, it sets the tone of all professional accomplishments. It may also act as a program committee, preparing presentations at meetings of the attending staff. It possesses full power to act and to speak for the organized staff between meetings of that body. Its membership may comprise the president and secretary of the staff with chairmen of the other standing committees, or it may be selected from the general group.

The joint conference committee or its equivalent, brings together trustees, the administrator, and medical staff members for consideration of matters of a medico–administrative nature directed toward better patient care. It should meet regularly with medical staff members and trustees alternating as chairmen. The administrator serves as secretary, assuming responsibility for the agenda and the preparation of minutes. To an increasing degree, such a group is recognized as the proper liaison between doctors and trustees. Its functions are confined to discussion rather than to definite action, any recommendations being referred to their proper sources.

According to the American Medical Association and the American Hospital Association

. . . such a committee should be a part of the organizational structure of every hospital. It should exist even where there is medical staff representation on the governing board. The representatives of this committee meet not as representatives of the departments from which they are chosen, but as members of the committee as a whole in the interest of the patient, the hospital, and the community.

The credential committee's chief responsibility is to explore the competence and moral character of applicants to any division of the medical staff, or for hospital privileges. This involves securing written references from physicians named by the applicant as well as careful checking of references from other sources. Similarly, the committee reviews staff members' credentials at the expiration of their appointment and recommends action to the executive committee. Occasionally recommendation for appointment is made by the medical director or chief of staff. In such instances the credentials committee should act on that recommendation.

The medical records committee assumes responsibility for maintaining proper medical records for all patients. Delinquencies are reported to the executive committee of the staff for action. Should its members be unsuccessful in handling the situation, the matter receives board attention. In larger hospitals each clinical department may review its own records and the committee selects for study certain ones picked at random.

The tissue committee provides assurance that the surgical procedures of the hospital are at a high level of performance. It reviews the pathological reports of all tissue removed from surgical patients. In some instances the responsibility of this committee has been broadened to decide whether or not the surgery was essential even when no tissue is removed.

Immediately following operative procedure the tissue is sent to the pathology laboratory where it is examined to determine whether it is normal or diseased. If it appears normal, or should there be any question about the surgery done, it is referred to the tissue committee with the entire case history. There must be a satisfactory answer to the question—Why was healthy tissue removed? Its removal may prevent it from becoming diseased; or, in repairing a diseased organ, it may be essential to remove healthy tissue. Much depends upon the history of the case.

Variance in the committee structure meets specific requirements. A medical audit committee may parallel or replace the medical records or tissue committee.

The medical audit assures accurate appraisal of the health care of patients. It constitutes professional service in accounting and passes judgment upon the quality of medical care by examining each physician's performance and tabulating his results. It primarily studies the correctness and substantiation of final diagnosis, the detection of errors in diagnosis, prescription of treatment, and the presence of complications whether recognized by physicians or as indicated by consultation.

A house staff committee considers applicants and assumes responsibility for the training of young doctors. A program committee may specialize in planning monthly staff conferences.

To assure the evaluation, selection, and proper use of medicinal agents, a pharmacy or therapeutics committee is essential. This is composed of physicians and pharmacists who evaluate new pharmaceuticals and decide which preparations will be stocked in the pharmacy. It may also develop a formulary to meet the hospital's needs.

The Joint Commission on Accreditation of Hospitals recommends a committee on infection control to study and make recommendations to reduce the number of infections in the hospital. Also with growing recognition of the importance of reducing unnecessary admissions and other misuses of hospital services and facilities, utilization committees are being formed. Such committees, composed of doctors, concentrate upon inappropriate admissions, under-stays as well as over-stays, delays in the use or over-use of diagnostic and therapeutic services, and delays in consultations and referrals. They time admissions to take advantage of hospital facilities, increasing weekend operation. They study patients under hospital care and review any cases questioned by Blue Cross. They provide assurance that all of the in-patient service is necessary, and could not be provided as effectively by some other facility. Among other benefits they encourage the closer involvement of doctors in hospital affairs.

The importance of utilization committees has been described as follows by Dr. Russell A. Nelson, president of Johns Hopkins Hospital and past president of the American Hospital Association,

> In the long run this utilization committee idea and its effect by education of the medical staff in my judgment will be the most important factor in the control of utilization. It will also have a very useful effect in bringing the medical staff closer to the financial and management side of hospital operation.

Properly organized, the medical staff has definite regulations at its disposal by which to exercise control over professional practice, thus lessening the need for board action. It is assumed that when the physician is granted a position on the medical staff of a hospital he agrees to abide by its bylaws, rules, and regulations. Yet this does not absolve the governing board of responsibilities in the event of infractions. Its obligation does not end with proper medical staff organization. It must see that the staff functions properly.

TEACHING AND RESEARCH

THOUGH HOSPITALS have been recognized for their teaching programs, particularly with doctors and nurses, they are not essentially educational institutions. Their accomplishments in these areas have been supplemented by colleges and universities. They have functioned as an important resource in medical education rather than serving as operators of medical schools. Although they will continue to participate heavily in medical and nursing education the trend is to assign such responsibilities to so-called "institutions of learning," with the hospital providing personal contacts with patient care.

It is logical that the hospital's educational program start with graduate training for interns and residents. Internship generally comprises a one-year assignment following graduation from medical school. Residency requires one to five years or more study with full-time appointment to a hospital staff, and leads to qualifications in a specialty. These trainees are students rather than employees.

The American Medical Association's Council on Medical Education and Hospitals approves hospitals for intern training and for residencies and fellowships in specialties as well as for educating x-ray technicians, medical records librarians, occupational and physical therapists, and medical technologists.

To qualify for intern training a hospital must have at

least 100 beds, an annual admission rate of 2,500 patients, and an average daily census of 85 patients exclusive of newborn. Also, its autopsy rate must be at least 25 per cent of total deaths and it must provide the intern with an adequate variety of services and proper supervision. For residents headed for practice in a specialty, and intending to qualify for certification, experience in an approved hospital is particularly important.

In hospitals approved for intern training the board of trustees sponsors an adequate program which the medical staff executes. Upon the chief of staff—in the absence of a director of medical education—falls the burden of developing a course of education that will insure a proper variety of work under experienced supervision. The better the training program, the less of a problem it becomes to attract the needed number of high-grade young doctors. Because the demand far exceeds the supply, the others take what is left.

Throughout his hospital service the intern is under the supervision of the staff. Success in establishing an educational formula that is recognized by the deans and faculties of the medical schools reflects added distinction upon the institution. Internship is not a convenience to the medical staff, but an important educational function.

Added prestige goes to the hospital that attains approval for intern or residency programs. The presence of a house staff enhances patient care and meets the needs for members of the attending staff interested in teaching.

Lack of formal intern or residency training need not necessarily reflect upon the hospital's standards. It may speak better for the institution that deliberately reduces or eliminates its residency program than for its neighbor that persists in continuing one under substandard policies. In the absence of such programs care of indigents must either be handled by the attending staff on a voluntary basis, or by a paid staff working full time.

Every hospital, large or small, can participate in some type of medical education. Staff meetings and committee activities may well include educational features with outside speakers participating. Clinical conferences, staff seminars, and journal clubs are similarly helpful in keeping staff members informed.

One hospital of 125 beds has made professional history by its weekly staff meetings. These constitute what amounts to postgraduate education, with each member kept up-to-date on advances in his particular field. Doctors in neighboring hospitals likewise have a standing invitation to participate.

On such occasions every case that presents a problem is reviewed. A blackboard is set up and a screen is provided for showing films. Occasionally a guest speaker is invited, although general discussion of specific cases has been found to promote greater interest than formal talks.

In addition to the need of educating and producing more doctors, provision must be made for continued education. Medical care is undergoing scientific, social, educational, and economic changes. In the past a doctor could hope to keep up-to-date by reading his professional literature or by attending occasional meetings of his professional groups. Today obsolescence increases every year. It has been said that at the present rate of progress, medical training will be outdated within five years.

How to provide leadership in a program of continued education for staff members becomes a problem. The answer is found in the appointment of a director of medical education whose function is to stimulate participation in educational opportunities. Such a program may be realized through affiliation with some neighboring center or teaching hospital in conducting seminars, clinical conferences, and workshops.

The director of medical education is a relative newcomer to professional ranks. He may serve on a part- or a full-time basis and may be salaried or unpaid. Someone possessing the necessary qualifications and basic interests may be found among present staff members. Otherwise he is brought in from the outside.

Among the desirable qualifications for such a post are experience in medical education, some teaching background, and administrative ability. The individual should be mature, scholarly, and an active member of the staff. In such a position he serves as liaison between the staff and the administration. He should be involved in all activities concerning patient care, community relations, and research.

Today there are some 1,000 full- or part-time directors of medical education and more than 350 are members of the Association of Hospital Directors of Medical Education. Despite the fact that this organization was founded, only a decade ago, it has demonstrated its influence on the progress of medical education.

The same evolution that is taking place in the training of doctors applies to the education of nurses. Traditionally the hospital provided the nurse with her sole opportunity for a professional career, constituting a three year course for high school graduates. From the concept of service with emphasis on vocational training, greater attention is now focussed on educational content. Better educated nurses are essential as medical practice becomes more complex. In consequence, the resources of the university or college will become more conspicuous factors.

Although in following such a pattern the amount of nursing service rendered to the hospital by the student is materially reduced, there are compensating factors. Assured of better educational facilities the hospital will gain by having more capable nurses. It leads to an ultimate effective team or group headed by the professional nurse and assisted by practical nurses and attendants.

The question of how big a hospital should be to maintain its own school of nursing has long been debated. There are institutions that by reason of their size, facilities, and financial resources cannot and should not undertake nursing education. There remains nevertheless the opportunity of setting up a program for the training of auxiliary aides to nursing service either independently or through affiliation with some agency engaged in supplying such assistants.

As a member of the management team the dietitian spends a substantial proportion of the hospital's dollar, and also practices a vital therapy. Conscious of the need to establish higher professional standards, the American

Dietetic Association's requirements for membership include a college degree with courses in basic physical and social sciences, foods and nutrition, and institutional management, followed by a year's internship in hospitals considered by the Association to offer well rounded training.

Other types of professional workers practice in the hospital and learn in the process, for the science of medicine and the care of the sick are never static. Professional education must be continuous.

Education leads to another highly important function of the modern hospital—the conduct of research. In this area the hospital with university, college, or medical school affiliation has definite advantage through its access to biological, chemical, and physics laboratories. Yet this need not discourage the average institution from conducting its own investigations and exploratory studies.

Every doctor, nurse, and technician has a role to play in the broader fields of research. Every trustee assumes the obligation to see that his institution is contributing its share.

Such contributions do not necessarily involve tremendous expenditures added to an already overtaxed budget. They become part of the daily responsibilities that every hospital worthy of its name assumes.

THE DOCTOR LOOKS AT THE HOSPITAL

BASIC CHANGES are taking place in medical practice that influence the doctor's attitude toward the hospital. Health care is now largely hospital centered, and the indication is that it will become more so. This automatically identifies the physician more closely with hospital policies, and those individuals responsible for establishing and maintaining them.

The doctor occupies a unique position in the hospital: Neither an employee nor a consultant, he is virtually an outside or independent contractor who renders service for which he is morally, and sometimes legally, responsible under auspices upon which he is completely dependent but over which he has little or no control. Although he has no vested interest in the enterprise, he is at the same time largely dependent upon it.

In the past, the doctor has seldom been consulted in the management of these institutions, a situation he has sometimes resented. Whereas too great involvement in administrative affairs might conflict with his professional advancement, he seeks recognition nevertheless as an active participant in the services the hospital offers.

As one medical staff member puts it:

There should be complete cooperation on all matters pertaining to the welfare of the patient and the advancement of the hospital. The doctor should have the interest of the hospital at heart if he is to have the interest of the patient at heart. It is a two-way street—medical staff members should have the cooperation of the board and the administration, and the board and administration should have cooperation from the medical staff.

Getting down to practical everyday affairs he adds:

Some administrators are immune to the physician's problems. They should try to recognize the headaches he encounters in parking, time of meetings, number of hours served in clinics. . . .

Frequently the doctor assumes his hospital responsibilities with little if any knowledge of administrative structure. His years of medical training have been spent in virtual exclusion from outside influences. He has worked and lived within the aura of medical science surrounded by individuals as remote from business procedure as he. Suddenly he finds himself a member of a group whose policy makers have little if any acquaintance with medical science or hospital techniques.

Recognizing the needs for orienting the staff member, one large university hospital conducts a program of six sessions constituting five group lectures and discussion periods with an individual conference with the administrator. During the first group meeting the chairman of the medical board, a trustee, and the administrator describe the hospital pattern. Other sessions are devoted to medical staff organization, functions of the board of trustees, professional standards, the educational program, the doctor's responsibility in communicating with the patient, cost of hospital care, etc. Frequently the last session is followed by a dinner attended by officers of the medical staff and the medical policy board.

The physician is a direct beneficiary of the hospital. It has improved his economic position through establishing high standards of patient care with modern accompanying facilities. Moreover through prepayment plans it has reduced the number of patients he otherwise would serve at no charge. Still, doctors remain concerned over the threat of being controlled, of interference in the performance of their duties, fear of a dominating board, or a paternalistic government ready to take over. As the hospital becomes the focal point of all health services the doctor sees his identity and independence threatened.

Is hospital service to be gauged by strict adherence to a budget, or by its accomplishments as written in the medical records? Some doctors feel they should be running hospitals, yet, if put to the test, they would be the first to acknowledge their limitations and to proclaim their dislike for managerial responsibilities. Not until the doctor gets the true picture revealing the lay board on one side, the medical staff on the other, and between them the administrator serving as coordinator, does he start to gain confidence.

The trustee similarly is not always happy about the situation. Because of his business background it is difficult for him to understand the physician's point of view yet each has the same objective—better patient care. The trustee is providing facilities for services which only the doctor can render. The patient's relationships, nevertheless, are with the physician rather than with the hospital which in acute situations can put management in second place.

For many years the relationship between doctors and hospital management was one of remote control. Contacts came through the administration. In the large institutions trustees and medical staff members were frequently strangers. Professional counsel advised against any member of the active medical staff serving on the board of trustees, an opinion which still prevails.

The recommendation that every hospital should include among its committees a joint conference group, broke down the barriers between lay and professional interest. It was recognition of the growing need for a team approach to hospital and health problems. Today, as already pointed out, the joint conference committee or its equivalent is essential for all accredited hospitals.

There are various approaches to the joint conference concept. One hospital has inaugurated what it calls its "kitchen cabinet." This committee corresponds closely to the function of a standing committee, but its informality makes it more effective.

Three members of the executive committee of the medical staff with three members of the executive committee of the board of trustees and the administrator meet at a downtown club for luncheon or dinner whenever it seems important to discuss certain policies. Having reached their conclusions, they decide what recommendations each group will refer to its constituent bodies for action.

To promote joint management and reduce misunderstandings another institution has formed what is known as a management council. This is made up of chairmen of the four clinical departments and the senior executive officer.

It operates on the general principles that the total effective management of a hospital requires the combined skills of those held accountable by the board of trustees for the quality and quantity of medical care rendered, as well as those accountable for the quality of the vehicle and its personnel. Authority must continue to be absolute in each discipline of professional management as designated by the board of trustees.*

Whatever the mechanics employed, the doctor is becoming more involved in hospital administrative affairs. This is in line with the trend toward concentration of medical facilities within the hospital. No longer can the physician fulfill his professional functions without the assistance of specialists such as the pathologist, radiologist, anesthesiologist, physiatrist, and specialists in physical medicine and rehabilitation. Increasing numbers of physicians, in addition to those engaged in such specialties, are becoming full- or part-time salaried employees. These, for the most part, are top staff physicians such as chiefs of obstetrics, gynecology, medicine, pediatrics, and surgery, and directors of medical education. For assuming such responsibilities they are entitled to compensation comparable to that of their fellows who are engaged in private practice. According to one survey, 99% of the general hospitals have one or more medical staff members under

* John M. Danielson, "Organization to Integrate the Medical Staff in Patient Care" from a paper on *The Impact of Changing Medical Practice on Hospital Administration,* published for Evanston Hospital, Evanston, Ill.

contract. Most of these are specialists, chiefly board certified men.

Another factor that identifies the doctor more closely with the hospital is the provision of office space made available to him either within the building or adjacent to it. This facility appeals chiefly to obstetricians, surgeons, internists and others whose work requires frequent use of hospital beds and diagnostic facilities. Such accommodations are advantageous in that they acclimate patients to the hospital atmosphere and reassure them that their doctors are within easy call.

The fears and suspicions that develop in the minds of medical staff members regarding hospital policies and management can be relieved through the simple process of opening doors that formerly have remained closed. Staff members should be made welcome at board meetings if they choose to attend. The same courtesy should be extended by the medical staff to the boards of trustees. Each group has but one objective—better patient care. Listening to one another's problems will prove illuminating.

The doctor should know something about the economic structure of hospitals. He is, or should be, a coordinating agent between the hospital and the community. He should have the facts about rising hospital costs in order to answer any questions regarding charges or any complaints about the services received. He should be sufficiently informed about hospital practice to explain the reasons for the rules and regulations that govern it. Any evidence of criticism or lack of endorsement on his part can breed suspicion and result in bad community relations.

The doctor serving on the staff of a voluntary hospital should possess allegiance to the institution and faith in its purpose. For this reason he should limit his hospital affiliations to one or two institutions.

The intimate contacts that develop between a staff member and the trustee he serves professionally can precipitate delicate situations. Physicians have been known to influence board action through such relationships. Some doctors are equally convinced that it is only the administrator who has the ear of the board president. Mutual understanding and dedication in meeting the patient's needs will eradicate such attitudes.

As he becomes more intimately involved in management affairs the doctor will look at the hospital more realistically. He will recognize that every institution cannot provide all professional services, such as deep therapy or open heart surgery. Economically it is unsound. Responsibility for overall health care must be shared with neighboring institutions and agencies.

At the same time the doctor will give his support to more efficient utilization of hospital services and thereby reduce the amount of bed care where possible. He will recognize the growing importance of the emergency department and out-patient clinics in the modern health care program. He will appreciate and respect the responsibilities assumed by the trustees and administrator in meeting new needs and will cooperate with them. When tension rises or differences of opinion become threatening, outside counsel can be invited to furnish unbiased opinions.

Every good hospital must adhere to professional standards with a well oriented medical staff, operating faithfully and efficiently according to the precepts set forth in the constitution and bylaws, a medical staff that is self-governing and that accepts the authority which the governing board invests in it. Under such favorable conditions there need be no fear of strained relationships between trustees and doctors.

6

Executive Direction

THE ADMINISTRATOR'S ROLE

THE ADMINISTRATOR serves as leader and counselor to the governing board in hospital and health affairs,
aids in formulating policies and directs the execution of
such policies. In public, non-voluntary institutions he
represents the government. In all institutions irrespective
of their sponsorship he acts as liaison officer between the
governing board and the medical staff. He is answerable
to the community for its most important public utility,
and he must therefore understand its social and political
climates.

Two contrasting factors in the hospital pattern need to
be harnessed together for an effective team approach—
the strictly business and the strictly professional. Between
the two is the administrator.

Executive skill, vision, and sound business judgment
coupled with professional knowledge and the ability to
adjust to others under all circumstances are essentials of
hospital leadership. Unlike business executives, however,
the hospital administrator frequently is too bogged down

with minor involvements to assume broader directives.

He must be a multifaceted individual assuming responsibilities for the operation of numerous departments. Some knowledge of financing is essential, including cost accounting, budget preparation, and the interpretation of financial reports. As buyer of thousands of different commodities he must know the principles of purchasing. Because he employs many types of labor, professional and nonprofessional, he must understand personnel policies.

In his capacity as professional counselor to his board the administrator needs to be skilled in the art of communication. Orientation programs for new board members as well as refresher courses for others are important to the best understanding of the problems involved. These may be conducted as individual hospital projects or under the auspices of local planning councils or hospital associations.

Board meetings provide an opportunity to acquaint the trustees with hospital affairs on local as well as regional and national levels. Fifteen or twenty minutes devoted to some educational feature or new technique by a member of the medical staff or a department head can prove stimulating.

The practice of sending out reports and financial statements in advance of meetings will promote more intelligent discussion and reduce time devoted to details. To the greatest degree possible, members should be informed in advance of subjects scheduled on the agenda so they may come prepared to enter into any discussions and to vote intelligently.

The hospital administrator needs to be an educator, for the modern hospital is an educational institution. Growing emphasis upon research requires the executive to keep pace with the latest developments in medical science.

He must be a leader for the board of trustees, the medical staff, the personnel, and the community. His influence spreads beyond the confines of the hospital's physical plant to adjoining areas where he plays a major role in developing closer coordination of health services.

Until 1933, little formal consideration was given to the aptitudes and qualifications of hospital executives. In that year, in Chicago, the first institute for hospital administrators was held, marking the initial step of the Committee on Education of the American Hospital Association toward more efficient hospital management. That same year witnessed the inception of the American College of Hospital Administrators.

Such efforts to raise the standards of hospital administration have resulted in educational opportunities hitherto unknown to those who would embark upon hospital careers. Today some 19 universities are offering graduate courses in hospital administration and hold membership in the Association of University Programs in Hospital Administration. These are: Army–Baylor University, Houston, Texas; University of California, Berkeley; University of California, Los Angeles; University of Chicago, Chicago; Columbia University, New York; Cornell University, Ithaca; Duke University, Durham, N.C.; State University of Iowa, Iowa City; Universidad Nacional Autonoma de Mexico; University of Michigan, Ann Arbor;

University of Minnesota, Minneapolis; University of Montreal, Montreal, Canada; University of Pittsburgh, Pittsburgh; St. Louis University, St. Louis; University of Toronto, Toronto, Canada; Medical College of Virginia, Richmond; George Washington University, Washington; Washington University School of Medicine, St. Louis; and Yale University, New Haven.

These courses, usually conducted under the auspices of schools of public health, of business administration or in graduate schools, are available to men or women with bachelor's degrees who want to devote two additional years to graduate education leading to a master's degree. The basic pattern is one year of academic training followed by one year as a resident in a selected hospital working under an experienced administrator. This is similar to a medical internship.

Executive directors of the schools, members of the Association of University Programs in Hospital Administration, meet at regular intervals to exchange ideas and opinions and to check their success in answering the needs of a changing management pattern.

Certain variations are found in these university programs. There is a trend toward requiring two years of academic work without the one year of residency. One program offers the student two years of academic training with three months' residency during the intervening summer. Another prepares the student for broader responsibilities by including in its year's residency a month in Blue Cross offices, a month in a community hospital and health center, and two weeks in a planning agency or council. For their services during the training periods the institutions or agencies involved offer the students a modest monthly stipend.

Following graduation the student embarks on his hospital career with the title of administrative assistant or in some instances assistant administrator. The ultimate objective of most graduates is a hospital of their own some six to seven years following graduation.

Whereas a master's degree is not essential to success in hospital management, it is a gauge by which board members evaluate candidates. Nearly 300 students are graduated each year and placed without too great difficulty. To an increasing degree, ancillary health services are opening up career opportunities. These include planning agencies, consultant services, hospital and health insurance plans, association programs, rehabilitation, geriatrics, and long-term illness facilities.

The complexities of hospital management raise the question: What prompts an individual to enter this field? The most common answer is the opportunity to serve others.

A frustrating business experience may divert the candidate to a more altruistic profession. One college graduate having sold insurance for several years became convinced that the career of a salesman was not sufficiently rewarding. At the suggestion of a friend who was engaged in hospital work he applied successfully to one of the university courses in hospital administration. Considerable sacrifice was involved in starting his education over again. Two or more years were required before he could contribute substantially to his family—a wife and two children. With persistence and some financial help, he won out with every promise of earning an adequate livelihood with the added recompense of serving the less fortunate.

Questionnaires sent to graduates of one university course to find out what motivated them to enter hospital work brought such replies as: "Opportunity to help fellow man"; "Opportunity to be creative"; "Opportunity to work with people"; "Opportunity to work in a medical environment." Security, status and financial rewards received the lowest scores.*

Hospital management in many respects is more demanding than most other executive responsibilities, as it is so closely involved with human emotions. No matter how skilled he may be in the techniques of management there are other less tangible qualities that determine the success of the hospital leader. He is judged by his measure as an individual, his willingness to give of himself to those who are suffering physical discomfort and mental conflicts, and his spirit in facing up to life.

SELECTING THE EXECUTIVE OFFICER

WHERE AND HOW to locate an administrator possessing the essential qualifications for competent management can become a major problem for the hospital

* Sherwin Z. Goodblatt, "Administration Graduates Make Good," in *The Modern Hospital*, December 1963.

board. The same confidence with which the trustee appraises the potentialities of an applicant for a business post fails him when he casts about for someone to assume responsibility for a hospital. Nor can he count too much on his associate board members, most of whom are similarly unfamiliar with the requirements of the position.

Help is available from various sources. Most obvious is the professional placement service conducted by organizations specializing in hospital, medical, and nursing personnel. Directors of hospital administration courses are prepared to make suggestions from the ranks of their graduates. Administrators of larger hospitals may have assistants whom they will recommend. Leaders in hospital work nationally, regionally and locally, also directors of local hospital associations and councils are available for advice. Professional hospital consultants and management counselors are a source of reference.

Several interviews are usually needed to estimate the individual's qualifications and to assure mutual appraisal. Where substantial traveling expenses are involved it is expected that the hospital will defray all costs. The interview constitutes a two-way street providing frank communication between the parties involved. The candidate has every right to know the truth regarding the hospital's professional standing, its board and medical staff relationships, long-range planning, and the institution's financial status. He would be wise to check the community's attitude toward the hospital and health care provided.

Responsibility for finding the right man rests generally with a committee appointed for that purpose headed by the president or other hospital officer. To encourage greater interest by doctors in the management pattern, the president or other representative of the medical staff might be invited to serve with the selection group.

The first step of such a committee may well be a formal job description of the position of chief executive officer. Next there should be an evaluation of the hospital's needs, based on present and future requirements. This would consider such facts as the institution's type and size, its present bed capacity, the extent of its teaching and research program, the composition of its board and medical staff, its financial position, and its reputation in the community and general area. Equally important are its future objectives, the extent to which it has engaged in long-term planning, and any steps it has taken toward coordination with neighboring hospital or health facilities.

The small hospital—one under 100 beds—has its own administrative problems. Some administrators view it chiefly as a stepping stone to broader opportunities. Yet in many respects the small hospital demands greater administrative competence than larger institutions where the chief executive has the backing of more experienced department heads. Furthermore the small hospital cannot compete with the salaries larger institutions offer. It has been suggested with good reason that certain smaller colleges might initiate courses in management as supplementary training for nurses. This would enable young women to "double in brass" in the capacities of administrator and nursing supervisor.

Men with nonprofessional backgrounds constitute the

majority of today's hospital administrators. An exception is the male nurse who, ambitious to broaden his career, may enroll in one of the graduate courses leading to a master's degree in hospital administration.

Other exceptions include female nurses, lawyers, pharmacists, engineers, teachers, clergymen, etc. Particularly significant are the increasing numbers of Roman Catholic nuns who are entering university programs in hospital administration. His medical background plus executive ability places the doctor in an enviable spot to gain top administrative rank in large medical centers with medical school or university affiliation.

As hospital management assumes the proportions of big business, the trustee seeks the same qualifications in his hospital administrator as he would in any business associate. The successful candidate is commonly the executive type, of good physical appearance, pleasing personality, in excellent health, direct in his approach, sufficiently mature to handle effectively any major situation yet young enough to hold promise of years of efficient leadership. Add to this one more quality—dedication to serve the public's health interest.

Trustees know from their own experience what business must pay for competent administration. With growing recognition of the need to provide more efficient hospital management, salaries of hospital executives are fast approaching those offered by industry.

For many years hospital administration was a poorly paid occupation, compensated for by fringe benefits such as housing, food, and other perquisites. Maintaining the administrator on the premises is now considered inadvisable barring extenuating circumstances. The same attitude applies to feeding him from the hospital kitchen. Occasionally a car is placed at his disposal for business purposes.

Preferred policy is to pay the administrator a salary commensurate with his responsibilities and let him maintain himself and his family where and how he chooses. No business executive is expected to live with his job 24 hours a day and neither should the hospital administrator. Because of the nature of the services for which he is responsible, it is particularly important that he be relieved from too constant and intimate contact with hospital atmosphere. Furthermore, the demand for space in most institutions precludes housing any more personnel than is essential.

Salaries vary depending upon the size of the hospital and its geographical location. According to one study, the four top ranking salary regions are the Middle Atlantic, New England, West North Central and Pacific.* A fair estimate of the salary range of hospital administrators starts with a low of $7,500 or thereabouts in very small hospitals to as high as $25,000 or $30,000 in larger institutions. Certain big medical teaching and research centers are known to pay $50,000 or more. Salaries of administrators possessing medical degrees are naturally higher than those having other backgrounds. Assistant administrators with a master's degree in hospital administration but with

* Miriam T. Dolson, Ph.D., *Today's Hospital Administrator—A Tentative Profile*, Sloan Institute of Hospital Administration, Cornell University, Ithaca, N.Y.

no practical experience start from $7,500 or $8,000 working up to as high as $10,000, $12,000, or $15,000 or even more in large institutions.

Before reaching a final decision on the appointment there should be unanimous agreement that in addition to his professional abilities the candidate is of sufficiently strong executive caliber to stand up under pressures and courageous enough to fight for principles he knows to be sound. There should be evidence too of his compatibility with the community. Case histories reveal innumerable instances where the newcomer has been unable to adjust to the local environment. For this reason the applicant's wife should also participate in the preliminary negotiations to assure herself of satisfactory housing for her family, congenial church affiliations, and good school facilities.

No formal contracts are customarily required between the hospital and its executive officer. The transaction is based on a gentleman's agreement and any termination of relations should be effective only with just cause and ample notice on both sides.

BOARD RELATIONSHIPS

IT IS NOT necessary to go back too far in hospital history to find the executive officer regarded as the "paid worker," or "innkeeper." His participation in board meetings was restricted to a brief report.

Today's hospital head, fortified by university degrees

and professional training, serves as counselor to the board. He attends all meetings of the governing board and its committees, and is excused only when action is taken on salary adjustments or other matters affecting him personally.

He may even become a board member, or, he may carry the title of executive vice-president or president. To fulfill such functions he is relieved of management details through the presence of associate administrators or assistants.

Titles assigned to the chief executive are a subject of debate. While recognizing the need to stress the importance of the position in the eyes of the hospital group as well as the public, any final decision should be based on whether this is merely a change in title or a change in responsibility. Does it involve some area of operation previously overlooked or assumed by other individuals or groups?

The so-called high turnover among hospital executives is frequently cited. Young men having their master's degree in hospital administration naturally seek positions offering greater responsibilities accompanied by more substantial financial remuneration. Too frequently they are influenced by the false conviction that a hospital's importance is gauged by its bed capacity. Ample evidence is present to disprove any such idea. It is not size alone that distinguishes an institution but the high standards and the varieties of its medical services.

A more basic reason for high turnover among hospital executives is their poor relationships with the hospital's trustees and medical staff members. The hospital president and his associates do not always grant the administrator the same business and social acceptance they would accord an executive officer in their personal enterprises.

The "employer vs employee" attitude is more frequently encountered in a community or rural environment than in larger metropolitan centers where everything becomes less personal. In outlying districts the hospital executive is in one sense a public servant. A stranger in town, an unknown quantity, his professional and personal lives are subject to public appraisal. Nothing is private, including his salary which may justifiably parallel or be above those of certain board members.

In smaller areas trustees frequently become the direct recipients of bad news and rumors concerning what happened to some neighbor when he became hospitalized. The hospital president is particularly vulnerable to complaints and demands. As a business executive he would automatically refer such matters to management. In hospital affairs, ruled largely by emotions he is tempted to take over personally.

One hospital president was summoned to the telephone one evening by an excited friend and generous contributor who poured out a lengthy diatribe on the lack of nursing care the gentleman's wife was receiving. Something must be done and at once. The president agreed. But what he did was in violation of all rules of sound business practice. Instead of referring the matter to the hospital administrator he proceeded to take it up personally with the nursing director with whom he was acquainted. It was not until the next day that the administrator learned the facts. Among them was an announcement of the nursing director's resignation.

Domination at the board level can become a threat to successful team work. This may be manifest through the presence of a clique of influential citizens or some individual seeking personal aggrandisement. Over zealous presidents have been known to request office space, which barring some extenuating circumstance, is bad practice.

The trustee group, commonly representative of civic leadership can exert pressure upon the administrator to adopt measures he knows to be detrimental to the best interest of the program. A trustee appointed because of his knowledge of some special subject—engineering, banking, or law—can unconsciously violate sound business practice by dealing directly with a department head.

Personal relationships between trustees and medical staff members serving them and their families can also make things difficult for the administrator. This may start with a casual comment by the medical chief during a golf game or at a party. The results become manifest at the next board meeting by strong opposition to the administrator's recommendation.

Under such conditions the administrator has three courses open. He can suggest seeking outside professional opinion, he can sit back and accept the situation, or he can start looking for another job. On occasion the latter solution has been known to be accepted philosophically by a board spokesman with—"It's easier to get another administrator than a good medical chief."

Respect for each other's position and responsibilities is

the key to good administrator–trustee relationships. The administrator must recognize the leadership that the trustee offers and the knowledge he possesses in specialized fields and should feel no hesitancy in seeking his counsel whenever necessary.

Recognizing the average trustee's lack of familiarity with hospital affairs some hospital executives have been tempted to make policy decisions on their own. Also less competent members of the profession, foreseeing problems developing through "over-educated" trustees, have deliberately refrained from encouraging their participation. Such attitudes are out of tune with modern concepts of hospital management.

The administrator's attendance at local, regional, and national meetings of hospital affiliated groups should be encouraged. Distinction accrues to him as well as to his institution when he is asked to serve in an official capacity in such professional bodies or when he is sought as a speaker before such groups.

On the other hand there is justification in the feeling that the administrator's principal attention should center upon his hospital. For this reason before accepting an invitation to serve as an officer of a national, state, or other professional organization, he should present the matter to his board indicating the extent to which he will have to be absent. Also he should be able to assure his board of the presence of assistants capable of carrying on during his absence.

The formerly common practice of permitting executives to accept consultation services for other institutions while trying to operate their own is now discouraged. Except in rare instances, responsibilities for the planning and conduct of one hospital is and should be a full-time job.

Personal relationships between the hospital administrator and his board members rest with the individuals involved, the type of community, and many other factors. No one answer will fit all situations.

Despite the inescapable fact that social and geographic barriers are fast disappearing, it is well to remember that familiarity breeds contempt. Personal judgment and discretion will indicate which is the right or the wrong approach. More than anything, complete frankness will contribute to good understanding between the administrator and his board. Fear, hesitancy, and suspicion contribute to the failures and the defeats.

Difference of opinion on policies and procedures are bound to develop. The administrator should offer his professional judgment honestly and sincerely. In his turn, the trustee has a right to challenge, to question, and to demand proof. As long as such procedure is fair and above board there can be no harm and there can even be benefits in such controversies.

It is the underground or subversive attacks that destroy the morale of the executive officer and wreck the whole structure. When confidence is destroyed there is little choice left but to change partners. And such changes should be faced courageously and acted upon promptly. Frequently boards lack the courage; they stall, they hedge, they hold back, fearful of criticism. As a result, a bad situation grows worse.

Frequently the administrator lacks faith in his convictions and in himself. He refrains from injecting himself into embarrassing positions. He deliberately conceals the truth from his board believing that its ignorance is his greatest protection to his survival in the job. Once the axe falls, as it inevitably does, he complains of injustices rendered, of autocratic control, and of lack of consideration and appreciation.

The same qualities that the trustee looks for in his administrator, the administrator has a right to expect of his trustees; interest, industry, fairness, tolerance, and good judgment, to mention only a few. To these, for good measure might be added a sense of humor and the ability to understand and to get along well with people.

WORKING WITH DOCTORS

MEDICAL STAFF PROBLEMS have long been the subject of discussion among hospital groups. According to report doctors can be difficult.

Bad relations between the administrator and the medical staff member may be attributed to numerous causes. By nature doctors resist regimentation, particularly under a management pattern that places control in the hands of laymen who, competent as they may be in business routine, lack knowledge of patient care. As the doctor views him, the hospital administrator is frequently young, unseasoned, uninitiated particularly to professional life.

Mutual understanding, respect, and confidence will go far toward eliminating friction between management and professional services. The doctor's first interest is his patient. The hospital must provide for the best interests of all its patients and of its community as well.

The doctor should know the reasons for certain hospital policies and why he must abide by them. Too often he criticizes rules and regulations without being told the reasons for their existence. His demands may be based on personal needs, or the needs of his area of work rather than upon the total hospital operation. On occasion he accuses the administrator of making decisions that should be the prerogative of the physician.

The administrator must be sensitive to the responsibility the doctor assumes and the tensions under which he works. He needs basic knowledge of the different aspects of patient care and how to evaluate professional ethics and performance. He should be familiar with medical terminology and with medical school curricula, enabling him to participate intelligently in medical staff meetings and technical conferences. His presence and participation in medical staff meetings are essential. Unfortunately this is not always universal practice.

One young administrator discovered that his predecessor had never attended staff meetings. This troubled him. Was he sticking his neck into a critical situation or was such an attitude based merely on tradition? Assured that the situation if handled properly could be met, he faced up to it. Within one year his presence was not only welcomed, but he was serving as the recording secretary.

There is a right and a wrong approach to medical staff relationships as many administrators have discovered.

Most misunderstandings may be attributed to lack of adequate communication. This is why joint conference committees are recommended. Their success, however, rests largely with the leadership exercised by the administrator. In addition to his own ideas he should be in a position to contribute from outside sources based on broader perspectives.

An invitation to the chief of staff to attend board meetings *ex officio* will further the team concept. A broader knowledge of hospital problems will benefit him as well as his associates. Two or three medical board members in rotation might be invited to attend each meeting of the board of trustees as guests.

Medical staff bylaws, frequently out-dated and inadequate in conforming with changing hospital policies, contribute to misunderstandings. Frequent review and appraisals will focus attention upon important issues such as the tenure of medical staff officers as well as their functions and responsibilities.

In addition to regular staff meetings, occasional conferences with committees and individual members will provide the administrator with opportunities for discussing matters of mutual interest. His door should always be open to those having complaints or seeking special consideration.

A common criticism doctors level at hospitals is that they are not told what is going on. To overcome such feeling, some administrators distribute a newsletter periodically to all staff members.

Staff meetings provide logical occasions to break news

such as changes in the physical plant, services pertaining to patient care, or admitting or billing procedures. The purpose is not necessarily to seek approval, but to describe proposed action before it is taken. Strong opposition to such changes may be referred to the joint conference committee for further discussion.

Inadequate orientation is the cause of many misunderstandings that develop. New staff members should be introduced to those in the hospital with whom they will be working. They should be made familiar with internal operation policies and the location of various departments and facilities. They should be told what services are available for patients and the procedures for obtaining such services. The organization and the operation of the medical staff should be explained along with what is required of the individual doctor with regard to teaching, working in the clinic, and emergency calls. Not only should staff members be conversant with hospital problems but they should be in a position to explain those problems to others with whom they come in contact, inside or outside the institution.

As part of their orientation in hospital affairs it would be advantageous to encourage doctors' attendance at local and state hospital association meetings. There they will get a picture of new trends and of present day problems. Mixing professionally as well as socially with the administrative group will give them a different perspective of the entire operation.

In establishing "social contacts" with medical staff members administrators should exercise caution. Playing favorites may well lead to future embarrassments. Friendly relations are best maintained on the group level, enabling delicate situations to be handled impartially. Tension becomes less acute over a cup of coffee or a sandwich at the coffee shop counter. Outside the hospital too, on the golf course notably, opportunities are provided for developing helpful channels of communication.

The administrator will win the doctors' respect by the way he handles controversial situations. The leadership he exerts must be firm yet never arbitrary. Great as the temptation may be to deal directly with the staff member found guilty of some breach of conduct, his better judgment may advise him against such action. Instead, he will see that the matter is brought to the attention of the joint conference committee. Should he continue dissatisfied with the results, it lies within his jurisdiction to report directly to the board. The board intervenes only in the exercise of its trusteeship and it should never interfere or dictate in the practice of medicine or surgery.

Under modern concepts of hospital management and operation the "difficult" staff member is less frequently encountered. A happy example of the mutual esteem now frequently shared by administrators and doctors is the action taken by one medical staff in electing the administrator an honorary member of the local medical society.

7
Auxiliaries and Volunteers

PAST AND PRESENT PERFORMANCE

THE HOSPITAL AUXILIARY exemplifies voluntary spirit yet duplicates the services of no other department or group within the institution. It is organized with the formal approval of the hospital governing board. Occasionally it appears as the "Women's Board," the "Women's Aid Association," or the "Society of Friends of the Hospital." This last appellation has one advantage of opening the field to men.

As a membership organization the auxiliary provides its own internal government, designates and controls the numbers and the types of membership, appoints standing and special committees, and operates as a separate but sustaining organization. It supports the program of the hospital under the guidance of the administrator in accordance with the policies formulated by the institution's board of governors. Contact with hospital management is maintained through the administrator, although a clause in the hospital bylaws gives the auxiliary president the privilege of attending board meetings *ex officio*.

Two broad areas of support constitute the functions of the hospital auxiliary—to serve, and to communicate. More specifically, these involve interpreting hospital service to the community, providing a source of volunteer aid, promoting and supporting auxiliary programs involving professional education and medical research, and fund raising. Such services are valuable to government sponsored institutions as well as to those operated under voluntary auspices.

The channels of interpretation as exemplified in auxiliary activities form a two-way medium of communication between the public and the hospital. Through this medium new concepts of hospital and health service are brought to the world outside. Similarly, outside reactions and ideas flow into the hospital. The fact that every auxiliary member is a potential ambassador of goodwill makes desirable as representative a group as possible.

The origin of the hospital auxiliary may be traced to the minutes of a meeting held on November 24, 1913, at the Pennsylvania Hospital in Philadelphia:

It was voted that permission be given the committee on social service to nominate to the board for their approval an auxiliary committee of ladies that can meet with them in consultation relating to their work, said advisory committee to have no executive power.

Such close affiliation between volunteers and medical social service departments still exists in some institutions, although this responsibility is now only one of a myriad of projects falling under auxiliary sponsorship. Medical social service has emerged through the years as a profession in its own right.

For many years hospital volunteer groups operated with little relationship to similar agencies. Their functions were social and extremely informal; their bylaws, if any, were reduced to the simplest terms. They met either in quarters assigned to them in the hospital, in neighboring church parlors, or in homes. By mending, sewing, rolling bandages, and soliciting modest funds they made their presence felt.

World War II helped change tradition. Members who previously had been involved only indirectly in hospital affairs soon found themselves performing tasks neither they nor anyone else would have thought possible.

Following the war, hospitals faced new problems. Fortunately there were large numbers of individuals serving as volunteers who knew what those problems were. Organization became the order of the day.

Gradually in different sections of the country auxiliary groups began working together, first at local, then at state levels. Then in 1949 the American Hospital Association recognized auxiliaries officially through the formation of a committee on women's auxiliaries as a unit of its board of trustees.

This committee or council numbering 12, is appointed by the Association president with board approval. He also designates a member to serve as chairman. Four committee members are appointed each year for a term of three years.

Dues for Association membership are based on the bed capacity of the hospital. They cover, in part, the services of a full-time secretary for the committee who, working with the members, develops programs designed to promote the hospital auxiliary in all activities that will contribute significantly to better hospital service. Through news letters, bulletins, work books, and manuals, auxiliary members are kept up to date on volunteer progress throughout the country. A monthly magazine "The Auxiliary Leader" is directed to their particular interests.

Such acknowledgment of its current and potential contributions lent new impetus to the auxiliary movement. Membership jumped by the hundreds with accompanying reorganization of the operation pattern. Recent figures of the American Hospital Association show approximately 2,000 auxiliaries as members representing over 2,000,000 individual participants.

This rapid growth reflects the expansion of hospital services, the greater utilization of hospital facilities, and the decreasing members of professionally trained personnel available. Volunteer contribution has helped offset the lag.

Every state has now organized, or is in the process of organizing, a statewide hospital auxiliary association. Each year during the American Hospital Association's annual meeting, official representatives from the state groups and representatives from individual hospital auxiliaries meet in separate and joint sessions with the sponsoring body.

Size of individual auxiliaries varies, depending upon

local needs and other factors. One rural hospital of slightly over 100 beds boasts some 2,000 members distributed among 35 units scattered throughout the surrounding territory. Annual dues of $1 or $2 are common practice, with sustaining memberships of $50 and life memberships of $100. These encourage a sense of belonging and in the larger groups represent substantial financial support.

Community chests influence to a degree the pattern of auxiliary fund raising. Such annual drives may place restrictions on individual hospital appeals, making it necessary to limit them to specific projects. Also, fund raising programs sponsored by the auxiliary should in no way conflict with major campaigns conducted under the leadership of the board of trustees. Any such projects should be discussed with the administrator and approved by the governing board. Basic profitable ventures for volunteer groups include the traditional social functions such as fashion shows, garden tours, and concerts.

The hospital coffee and gift shop assures good returns under competent management. It is also valuable for its convenience for visitors, staff members, and employees, and the congenial atmosphere it creates.

Photographs of babies taken soon after birth have under favorable circumstances proved similarly profitable on two counts—goodwill and financial return. The services of a beautician are a morale booster and a good business venture, as are television rentals and facilities for supplying flower arrangements.

Financial benefits accruing from auxiliary enterprises

are allocated usually to specific projects agreed upon by the group in conjunction with the administrator. Special equipment offers a wide variety from which to choose. Furnishings and interior decoration are likewise appealing, with the presence of professional guidance to attain best results.

The well organized auxiliary serves as the focal point of volunteer effort, becoming an important source of workers who are screened and assigned certain in-service responsibilities, frequently by a professionally trained director. It is not essential that a volunteer become an auxiliary member nor is the volunteer program always organized through the auxiliary. Similarly, all auxiliary members are not in-service volunteers; some staunch supporters of the hospital merely pay membership dues. Others concentrate on fund raising projects and outside activities that possess public relations value. The pattern of operation depends upon the hospital and the community.

Hospital volunteers provide something that money cannot buy. Their presence is an inspiration to doctors, nurses, and hospital personnel, to say nothing of patients and visitors. They create an atmosphere of warmth and friendliness.

Such service is not confined to the sick room itself. It may start in the hospital foyer at the reception desk or admitting office. Volunteers may register, guide, and direct clinic patients, prepare charts for doctors, make return appointments, and take time out to divert a restless child with a toy. In the x-ray department they fulfill assignments in addition to instructing patients and providing their transportation. Blood banks, library services, and music therapy are other outlets for volunteer effort.

ORGANIZATION AND BYLAWS

THE TYPE of auxiliary organization depends on the size and character of the institution and of the community. To be effective it must be coordinated with the hospital's corporate structure. This involves adequate comprehension of the importance of voluntary participation by the board of trustees at the policy making level and the administration. Full potentialities can be attained only through well defined channels of communication between the board, the executive head or his representative, and the auxiliary president. Close relationships are assured by inviting the auxiliary president to attend board meetings with or without vote, also placing the administrator on the auxiliary's executive board *ex officio*.

Auxiliary bylaws, like hospital bylaws, too often are outdated and apply to times passed rather than to modern aspects of hospital and health services. Flexibility is essential, requiring opportunities for periodic review and amendment.

The presence of certain cliques and autocratic groups of senior citizens can discourage the participation of younger and less well established members. The auxiliary constitutes a community program to which all interested individuals should be made welcome and committed to the stated purpose as designated in the bylaws.

Auxiliary officers follow the usual pattern—president, preferably two vice-presidents, recording secretary, corresponding secretary, treasurer, with such assistants as seem necessary. Rotation of officers and committee chairmen is essential to provide fresh ideas and to broaden community interest and participation.

In the conduct of auxiliaries as elsewhere, the temptation is to appoint too many committees. Certain basic groups are essential to successful operation; others may better be eliminated or put on an ad hoc basis. Because of the rapid changes occurring in health care and hospital organization and administration, a committee for which there is justification today may be found obsolete tomorrow. Competent direction is always conscious of modern trends and reassigns members from one area of responsibility to another as seems best.

Four standing committees form the basis of the auxiliary's organization plan. These are: executive, nominating, membership, and finance. They may be supplemented by others such as bylaws, fund raising, legislative, coffee and gift shop, patients' library, public information and education, pictures, program, social service, thrift shop, and volunteer service. All manner of combinations of these working areas may be useful depending upon local conditions.

Originally, the responsibility for the in-service program was assumed by a committee for that specific purpose. With the growing acceptance of departments of volunteer service the post of salaried director has been created. In addition to basic qualifications, short training courses are provided for those who would enter the field such as that conducted under the auspices of Columbia University's Center for Hospital Continuation Education in New York City. Four weeks of intensive training includes lectures, seminars, workshops, and field trips under the supervision of faculty drawn from Columbia and other universities.

The director of volunteers, like other department heads, works under the direction of the administration with close affiliation with the auxiliary president. She recruits and assigns applicants for volunteer service and is responsible for their conduct and performance. In small hospitals where it may not be practical to provide a salaried director, equivalent responsibilities are assumed by the chairman of the auxiliary committee on volunteer service with the approval of the administrator.

Special or ad hoc committees are assigned to meet specific needs. Having accomplished their purpose, generally some short-term project, and having submitted their report, they are disbanded. Committees generally have a chairman and no less than two vice-chairmen. Particularly important is having both officers and committee chairmen representative of the region.

The age span of auxiliary membership, unless handled with discretion may lead to embarrassing situations. Younger women searching for an outlet for their abilities and energies frequently inquire—"How old must one be to become eligible for hospital service?" Casting an appraising eye over many auxiliary gatherings one sees the justification for such a question.

That life for the auxilian need not start at 50 was discovered many years ago. To overcome any feeling of frustration on the part of younger women who would join volunteer ranks, some hospitals have organized junior groups. This plan has proved successful to the point where an embarrassing question arises—"When does a junior cease to be a junior?"

One central body sufficiently broad in scope to offer inducements to all ages would seem to be the answer. Occasionally encountered is a situation where several groups, representing different factions, are actually competing with one another and in consequence destroying the total effect of volunteer support.

Volunteer service may be drawn from two other important areas—men and teenagers. Hospital service offers a definite outlet for the talents and training of men forced to retire at a comparatively early age. Granted their reluctance to become associated with what ostensibly is a women's group, they can serve without explanation under the auspices of the volunteer department.

Because hospital auxiliaries require rejuvenation, replenishment, and reactivation, the potentialities of teenagers deserve attention. Not only in terms of service but as part of their educational program young people of high school age have much to offer. Closer acquaintance with health careers or volunteer service initiates them to career opportunities. Through extra attentions to patients, serving food trays, doing errands, they can give rewarding service.

AUXILIARY–HOSPITAL RELATIONSHIPS

THE HOSPITAL AUXILIARY renders service in any manner that the board of trustees and the administrator may recommend. Its position as an integral part of the hospital pattern is measured by the degree of cooperation and communication between it and the administrative staff.

Precise functions of the various groups involved need to be clarified and to be brought into close and harmonious relationships. Boards too frequently rate the auxiliary according to the sums it produces for building or expansion funds, or other special needs. They know little about the other less spectacular contributions members are making which may have equal or even more significance. They fail to evaluate the importance of volunteer service in providing the extras the hospital could not otherwise afford. They underestimate the extent of goodwill such workers can generate as interpreters of health services in the community.

Many boards accept the presence of the auxiliary president at their meetings as a concession to *the ladies*. More likely than not, any report on the group's activities is the last item on an already overcrowded agenda.

To promote closer relationships between the board and the auxiliary, a woman may be appointed to the board who, if not actively identified with auxiliary activities, is representative of the community and knows what is going on. Such a policy works two ways. It is just as important

that the board knows what is happening in auxiliary circles as it is for auxiliary members to know what goes on in
the board room.

Administrator–auxiliary relationships have not always
been as harmonious as may be desired. To be just to administration, it may be said that any management pattern
that includes workers who cannot be treated as employees
presents problems. Fortunately, modern concepts of personnel relations within the hospital structure are changing
such attitudes.

The lay person who transgresses a bit is not always to
blame. More likely than not any infraction of rules comes
from excess enthusiasm, or from lack of sufficient orientation to the hospital's special demands.

Many breakdowns in the relationships between the
hospital and the auxiliary may be attributed to misunderstandings. A member may make demands upon the administration that to her seem completely justified. Once
she is made to recognize that she is just one of a group
and that her particular interests are only part of the overall picture she will in most instances concede the point.

Fortified by educational programs leading to a master's
degree, administrators are now better prepared to handle
voluntary participation. Happy relations exist today between many hospital executives and their auxiliary heads.
Recognizing the benefits of such support the administrator responds in the spirit with which it is rendered, appearing personally or sending a representative to auxiliary
meetings and special events.

It should be recognized by trustees, medical staff members, department heads, and even the humblest worker that the auxiliary is an integral part of the hospital. They should be apprised of its position on the organization chart showing the auxiliary president as accountable to the board of trustees through the administrator.

Similarly every auxiliary member should be made familiar with lines of authority within the hospital, particularly relationships between the trustees, the administration, and the medical staff. She should recognize that all matters affecting hospital operation rest with the administrator by reason of the authority delegated to him by the board of trustees.

In their contacts outside the hospital both auxiliary members and in-service volunteers reflect their own attitudes towards its affairs. Is their approach positive? Are they prepared to match stories of unfortunate incidents with the happy situations that occur daily? Good public relations are quickly wrecked over a cocktail or a cup of tea. Matters of service deficiencies or personal failure are better discussed in the administrator's office than at a card party.

The importance of relationships within the hospital and spreading out into the communities is becoming increasingly apparent. The objectives of health care are broadening and expanding with each new year. To attain those objectives requires united action by all hospital groups— policy makers, administrators, medical staff members, auxilians, and volunteers.

PATHS TO NEW GOALS

HOSPITALS WERE ONCE CONDUCTED as charities to meet the needs of the sick poor. Beneficence, characterized by donations to the under-privileged was the motivating spirit of carefully screened citizen groups. Such personal attitudes and group philosophies are now outdated. Today these institutions meet the health needs of all classes of society and must invite broad community support.

Having long ago demonstrated their abilities in inaugurating social service programs, auxiliaries have potentials as yet unexplored in the ever broadening areas of health education and research. New approaches remain to be developed to preserve human values in a scientific atmosphere.

The presence of too many separate membership groups, each with its own interests, can create competition for support within the hospital, and confusion outside from multiplication of appeals for participation and membership. Unification of efforts will prove of great value to the total hospital program. Some auxiliary leaders view with mixed emotions the operation of an in-service group operating as a hospital department under trained directorship. The director of volunteer services, on the other hand, rooting for the in-service team, may fail to recognize the need of community understanding and financial support. Complete success can be assured only through greater

unity between inside and outside interests, always with
patient care as the common objective.

An insular attitude has characterized hospital groups in
general. Their dedication too often is to one institution—
"our hospital"—rather than to overall community health
care. Planning of auxiliary and volunteer programs should
follow the trend toward coordination of health services,
assuring a chain of agencies working together to provide
comprehensive health care from cradle to grave, available
at the lowest possible charges. Programs should also take
into account the extension of patient care into the home,
in conjunction with members of the home-care team. In
such capacity volunteers stay by the bedside while a
member of the family is absent, do mending, or perform
other simple household tasks. Whether such services are
provided under voluntary auspices or some government
agency, there is need of citizen participation.

The volunteer's activity does not end with today's contribution, but has consequences for tomorrow, next year,
and the years to come. To assure success involves encouraging the participation by juniors or teenagers, introduc-
ing them to the rewards of serving others, to say nothing
of career possibilities in professional areas.

It is often difficult to interest young married women in
hospital work, particularly those with home and family
responsibilities. They may be quite responsive, though, to
the advantage in-service offers in teaching volunteers how
to help adjust children to hospital treatment and care and
to the role of the parent in such situations.

A tremendous area for recruitment of volunteers lies

among the growing ranks of retired citizens. Drawing upon their various business and professional backgrounds, men have substantial contributions to offer. Assured proper placement and guidance, they will find satisfaction in helping in such capacities as taking patients to and from x-ray departments, moving and turning patients, assisting in blood banks and business offices, writing letters and doing errands for elderly patients, and helping to feed cardiac sufferers. By helping others, they soon learn they are helping themselves.

The trend to establish satellite hospitals in out-lying areas as branches of large urban institutions opens new opportunities to recruit volunteers. Such distribution of health care will encourage greater participation by local volunteers since they will be spared hours of travel to and from their posts.

Various sources may be tapped in recruiting volunteers of both sexes and varying ages—private clubs, schools and colleges, churches, local junior leagues, fraternal orders, boy and girl scouts, personnel directors of business organizations, and chambers of commerce. Local radio and television networks will help broadcast volunteer needs and opportunities.

Once adequate numbers of volunteers are assured, proper direction is critical. Orientation to hospital routine implies more than mere acquaintance with institutional service and physical layouts. It entails recognition of professional ethics. In-service workers, particularly, should know not only what to say about what goes on within the building's four walls, but what not to say. Information may come to them unsolicited, which if divulged would cause embarrassment to others. They share the same trust as that pledged by doctors, nurses, and other professional workers.

Hospital interpretation is not to be confused with the recordings of local chit-chat. Final results will be positive only to the degree that the individual is initiated to the hospital setting, as well as to her own particular duties. These duties must be clearly defined and integrated into the entire service pattern. Continued education also is required to keep members informed on new developments in health care.

Meetings of auxiliary groups present excellent opportunities to provide members with broader perspectives. Too frequently program committees try to furnish entertainment rather than to inform. As interpreters of hospital service to the community, these citizens need first-hand knowledge of departmental functions and relationships between various professional groups. With this objective in mind, certain department heads might well be invited to explain the operation of their particular areas of service. Doctors too, should be invited to describe interesting cases. All volunteers will gain from knowledge of the work of the institution in the areas of education and research.

Leadership as exemplified in the president and committee chairmen is a major factor to the success of auxiliary functions. To be a successful leader, the executive officer must know the goals to be reached and along what paths she must direct her constituents to attain these objectives. This demands knowledge not only of the functions of the modern hospital and its relationship to other health facilities, but also the basic requirements of executive management. An abundance of sources are at her disposal from which she may gain such knowledge—lectures and seminars on group dynamics and leadership, books on technics of management and group direction, and articles on affiliated subjects in professional journals.

High on the list of requisites for any successful leadership is interest in all types of people, an innate desire to help them, a sensitivity to their problems and emotions, and frankness, courage, and kindness in facing delicate situations muted with kindness.

Above all else, the leader requires patience. She will not push too hard or obviously, but will work persistently to gain whatever ends she believes to be right. She will recognize the auxiliary for what it is and what it should be—a lay or voluntary group representing a cross-section of the community and working together harmoniously to establish and maintain high standards of health care.

The great advances made in medical science, with the high mechanical excellence of modern professional equipment, are helping to meet the physical needs of hospital patients. They can never serve as substitutes, however, for the human touch, that warmth of understanding which answers the social, emotional, and diversional needs of the patients. That is the privilege of those who volunteer their time, their interest, and their support.

PART THREE

Design for Community Health Needs

8

Developing the Program

ECONOMICS OF HOSPITAL CARE

THE ECONOMIC structure of voluntary hospitals has changed materially during the past half century. Originally each institution assumed responsibility for its financing through the beneficence of board members, popularly designated as philanthropists, plus public subscription and revenue from patients. To a modest degree government shared the burden of care of the poor.

As the public demand for hospital service grew, the consumer began to assume greater financial responsibilities through the creation of voluntary insurance plans, Blue Cross and Blue Shield notably, and later, commercial insurance coverage. Such support gave added impetus to the hospital picture, enabling it to grow in size as well as complexity. New institutions opened their doors; additions were made to existing structures. People who never before were hospital-conscious took advantage of the services offered, particularly semi-private accommodations made available through Blue Cross.

Despite its distinguished record, Blue Cross has become a target for criticism—an attitude that may be expected when the public's pocketbook is threatened. Accusations in the daily press claim the presence of mismanagement and inefficiencies. A warning finger has been pointed at unjustifiable building expansion, particularly in acute and general beds, with little provision for preventive, rehabilitation, and mental facilities. Little has been done to encourage coordination of facilities on a community or area-wide basis. Certain admissions are unnecessary and many patients remain longer than is justified. Business procedures have not kept pace with modern trends. The public is now demanding standards and controls to avoid excessive costs or misuse. Charges have been made that the voluntary system as it is operated today has grown obsolete. Blue Cross officials admit that there is some truth in these claims. Many items specifically labeled may be traced to "growing" pains.

Prepayment and insurance plans are being studied objectively on many fronts. Are they meeting the needs of all requirements of the population? Is the scope of their benefits sufficiently broad? What is being done to include post-acute facilities, drug and dental care? Are overheads kept at a minimum assuring maximum amounts for the benefit of the patient?

Definite steps to find the answers to these and other questions have been taken by certain state officials. New York, for example, through the Governor's Committee on Hospital Costs headed by Marion D. Folsom, formerly Secretary of Health and Education and Welfare under President Eisenhower, made recommendations that might well prove the salvation of Blue Cross. Mr. Folsom presented his conclusions bluntly. "If costs were not controlled hospital insurance would be prohibitive."

The formula under which Blue Cross reimburses hospitals for care rendered was a subject of question. Instead of basing payments on audited costs he urged that the method should provide "a strong incentive for the hospital to reduce the cost of operation without reducing the quality of care."

One specific recommendation was to remove retired people from Blue Cross and put them under Medicare, the federal plan for hospital insurance under Social Security.

Other suggestions were to:

(1) Have government assume all costs of hospitalized welfare patients.

(2) Extend Blue Cross to hospital outpatients, nursing home and home care patients.

(3) Form community hospital planning councils.

(4) Revise Blue Cross hospital-payment formulas to encourage them to cut costs without reducing quality.

(5) Shift medical training costs from hospitals to educational systems.

(6) Improve hospital efficiency by releasing patients as quickly as possible, sharing facilities, and improving business practices.

Well aware of the public's attitude, Blue Cross heads have faced the problem realistically. Recognizing the impact of Medicare on hospital and health economics, they have produced interesting ideas on their reimbursement policies.

In one rural county served by two hospitals, the Colorado Hospital Service is experimenting with capitation reimbursement. Instead of paying the hospitals per day of care, it pays them per member. Blue Cross members are not billed for services and instead Blue Cross distributes to hospitals the dues contributed by subscribers. In consequence all problems associated with case-by-case approvals and rejections, claims administration, and billings are avoided. During the first year of the experiment, the hospitals' reimbursement showed a marked increase from the amount which would have been received on the former per day basis. The total number of in-patient days per 1,000 members in the county dropped by 7.5 per cent from the previous year, whereas this ratio rose 3.5 per cent for all subscribers in the state.

This plan was started on a trial basis and is still in the process of evaluation. It is nevertheless in line with the opinions of many leaders, including the American Medical Association which has suggested that

> Communities must direct less of their thinking to additional beds and more to the organizational arrangements and facilities which will provide a continuity of care to most effectively meet their health needs—meaning that the right patient should be receiving the right service at the right time.*

The social security taxing mechanism for financing the health care of the aged has now become a reality. An expansion of the Social Security insurance program, Medicare provides hospitalization, nursing home care, home nursing, and out-patient diagnostic services for all Ameri-

---

* American Medical Association, *A Look At Hospital Construction,* Chicago, 1964.

cans over 65 years of age. It also provides a supplementary federal program of insurance covering a major part of the doctors' bills and other health costs at a charge of $3.00 a month in premiums which would be matched by federal appropriations of about $600 million dollars a year from general tax revenue.

The full impact of Medicare cannot be estimated until it has been in operation for a year or more. Some envision it as a blessing in disguise for Blue Cross subscribers. Relieved of the high risk category of those of 65 and over, voluntary insurance plans should find it easier to keep down rates for subscribers. This is not to be taken as assurance that Blue Cross rates will be reduced. With hospital costs still rising at a rate of 6 per cent annually, reduction in premiums is unlikely. It does represent however a saving for Blue Cross groups. For hospital people, Medicare presents a myriad of problems some of which are in the course of being studied. Others will not be obvious until after the legislation becomes effective.

One fact is evident. The medical system of the country is not geared at the present time to care for the increased demand that will be placed upon it by Medicare. Hospital facilities will be over taxed. The burden will be even greater, however, for nursing homes and those hospitals involved in extensive psychiatric care.

The Medicare program is based on the premise of transferring patients from high-cost beds into low-cost accommodations. Figures show that at present 9,700 nursing homes are providing such care. It is estimated that by 1970, 40,000 will be needed.

The most critical phase of the situation is the lack of physicians, surgeons, and nurses. Already the shortage is alarming. Similarly, more dietitians, physical therapists, technologists, and other professional workers will be needed.

Hospital management views with alarm the complicated record keeping systems that will be necessary. Separate bookkeeping sections may have to be set up to handle Medicare cases or to integrate the Medicare charges and payments system with their present processing machinery. Under the voluntary health insurance section of Medicare, separate bookkeeping may be required. Such bills will not be paid by the government but by "fiscal intermediaries," meaning Blue Shield, union medical plans, group health plans, or possibly commercial insurance companies.

Another problem surrounds the handling of Medicare patients' charges for the services of pathologists, radiologists, anesthetists, and physiatrists. Following long and tough debates in Congress, hospital based specialists are under the voluntary health insurance jurisdiction and may bill their patients individually.

What will be the effects of Medicare upon the quality of medical care? Some leaders hold the opinion that it may limit the drive to elevate standards. Many agree that changes in the manner in which doctors practice medicine are inevitable. From the experience of other countries practicing socialized medicine, it seems that once the fact becomes established that government is paying the bills, the demands for service increase.

WITH AN EYE TO THE FUTURE

THE NEED FOR A coordinated system of hospital and health care is not new. It was clearly indicated in the Hospital Survey and Construction Act of 1946, otherwise known as the Hill–Burton Act. This emphasized the benefits of affiliation between small hospitals in rural areas with larger institutions.

Such regional planning was based first on the concept of a teaching hospital serving in conjunction with affiliated hospitals; second, a general hospital of 100 or 150 beds; and third, small hospitals and health centers.

Some 15 years ago an interesting experiment in coordinating rural hospital facilities was attempted in northern New York State. Three small modern hospitals were erected in communities approximately 40 or 50 miles apart. The administrative pattern comprised one executive officer and three local boards. This development was watched with considerable speculation. To some it was the answer to health service for a rural region having a population of some 40,000 in winter and 50,000 during the summer months. To others, it was an administrator's nightmare and it proved to be so until the pattern took definite form.

Today the service has matured as one hospital of approximately 175 beds, geographically separated. One administrator assumes overall direction of the three units from the central hospital where such functions as purchasing, accounting, menu planning, and laundry facilities are centered. Management assistants represent him at each of the other hospital buildings in the dual capacity of administrator and director of nursing. An overall board formulates policies in conjunction with the three local boards.

Community grouping of hospitals has many advantages. Each can contribute a specialty service making up the total health care. It avoids duplication of expensive equipment and reduces the number of highly skilled workers.

The future of smaller hospitals, particularly those in metropolitan areas is debatable. According to city planners, all new hospitals in this classification should contain at least 200 beds.

The management pattern of hospitals is in a state of transition. It is composed of numerous professional groups fulfilling their functions as separate units, too frequently with little awareness of their relationships to others. Such traditional concepts of management are now being critically examined with recognition of the need to plan and to work toward broader concepts of overall service. Greater emphasis is being placed on departmental coordination, assuring better understanding among employees of their mutual work problems, the responsibilities of the policy makers, and administration.

To promote closer working relationships one hospital assigns department heads to serve as recorders for committee meetings of the board. While not involving the trustee in the operational details of the particular department, it enables him to ask questions and gain first-hand knowledge of interdepartmental operation. In turn it acquaints the department head with board functions.

Advances in this direction are becoming more conspicuous as the administrator assumes a position of greater influence. Strengthened by his educational background, reinforced by supplemental educational opportunities provided by professional groups and advanced training in management, his role is becoming increasingly vital. His concept of organizational structure must be based on the hospital as a whole. He must serve as a planner or organizer, rather than as a departmental operator, leaving routine management to assistants.

Better coordination between the hospital and the community implies careful study of its health needs with recognition of changing trends. The transition from traditional family residential areas to multiple housing developments will bring new patterns of health care.

Extended use of emergency rooms and clinic facilities is expanding for several reasons: services are cheaper than those in doctors' offices; doctors are not always available when needed; and many people have no regular family physician.

This development poses two questions: How can such clinic service best be rendered and what agreements can be reached with physicians to provide complete emergency care? Without proper professional coverage the lives of patients may be endangered, with consequent loss of public confidence and good-will.

One hospital has signed contracts with licensed physicians for guaranteed coverage of their services. Fees are charged by the physicians' group and the hospital guarantees a satisfactory income.

Hospital design of the future is rapidly changing. Some recommendations call for "putting the patient on the belt." This means mechanization to the greatest extent possible. The efficiency of such planning is argued by institutions that have reduced their employee ratio to correspond to the total number of beds, from 2.4 employees per bed to 1.5. Such opinion bows nevertheless to the uncontested truth that a machine should not replace services that human beings can better perform.

From the patient's point of view what will the picture be ten, twenty or thirty years hence? Small, private, air conditioned rooms will predominate. The bed may well become the entire room. Fully equipped and appropriately enclosed, it will have its own medically prescribed and automatically maintained atmosphere. No upper sheet or blanket will be required, for circulated air will maintain the desired temperature. Frozen food will be stored in the patient's own individual wall freezer, cooked automatically, a meal at a time. Patients will use disposable cellulose, fibre linens, and will eat with disposable utensils. Nearly everything will be disposable or converted to some other use.

Even today some patients are provided with finger-tip control of room and bed lighting and heating and cooling systems, and an all electric bed and automatic window curtains. A bedside console provides everything including tissues, telephone, bedpan, and extra blankets.

Equally dramatic are advances made in saving lives.

Who could have envisioned a few years back a surgeon opening the human heart, stopping its beat, and gaining an unobstructed view of that organ, being able to restore it to motion? Only the presence of a heart–lung machine that takes over the oxygenation and pumping of blood through the patient's body, handled by a team of eight to twelve trained specialists, could perform such modern miracles. At one time, when a patient appeared to have suffered a fatal heart attack, doctors would have shaken their heads in despair. Today they apply an electric device known as a *defibrillator*. Through electric shock, the heart can resume normal rhythm.

To help identify brain tumors and encephalitis, meningitis and the degree of strokes, the device known as an *electroencephalograph* is used by many hospitals. Among other important equipment is a machine that measures pressure on eye nerves in the diagnoses of glaucoma. Eye splinters and bullet fragments are removed electronically and electric incubators automatically control the humidity, temperature, and oxygen intake of premature babies.

While the patient is benefitting from these and other advances in professional techniques no less remarkable innovations are taking place behind the scene. The clinical laboratory is becoming automated. One remarkable machine will perform fifteen or more tests using one small sample of blood. X-ray films are processed automatically. Motion picture films made with x-rays enable the radiologist to study internal organs without use of the fluoroscope. Automated transportation systems are used to deliver supplies throughout large buildings. Current experiments indicate that the day is not distant when diagnoses will be made by computer. Computers are already being used to aid the nurse in giving medications to patients at the proper time.

Already the automatically controlled elevator is accepted as part of everyday life. The same principle is now applied in hospitals to drug compounds, food dispensing machines, pneumatic tubes, and other items of equipment. Computer systems now process accounts receivable, pay roll, and inventory operations in many of the larger hospitals.

Centralized, engineering controlled systems provide benefits in manpower savings. This has been demonstrated by equipment installed in one large medical center which links 19 buildings. At a compact desk-size central console, one man monitors the mechanical equipment for 1.4 million square feet of critical hospital areas, some of them nearly a mile away.

Monitoring systems are successful in labor and delivery rooms where they count the frequency of labor pains. Sometimes they can distinguish between real and false labor. Elsewhere they automatically measure and record the temperature, pulse rate, respirations, and blood pressure of twelve or more patients at a given time. Only one nurse is needed. An alarm system sounds if any recording reaches danger levels.

Circular patient units built around the nurse's station assure closer surveillance of patient needs. Escalators in certain places prove popular with the staff, visitors, and some patients, leaving elevators free for transporting supplies and other uses.

Temptation lies in the fascinating array of these and other new devices and techniques that are appearing in increasing numbers. Department heads, staff members, and administrators are susceptible to the wonder stories recounted by ambitious salesmen. The truth comes later, and sometimes shows insufficient preparation or understanding of the equipment involved or the cost of skilled workers to handle it. The logical question is: Will it pay? This is too often overlooked in the enthusiasm of keeping up with the times.

Modern trends in health care, needs, and facilities must be measured carefully by trustees, administrators, and medical staff members. They need to be considered in relationship to the individual hospital and to area specifications and demands. Blueprints should be prepared and should be acted upon only after careful study. These should bear evidence of some knowledge of the regional and national picture.

The need to find qualified individuals as sources of guidance in expansion or renovation plans was recognized by the American Hospital Association in 1948, when it encouraged the formation of the American Association of Hospital Consultants. Membership in this group requires at least ten years' experience in the general field of hospital administration with three years of consultation work either on a full- or part-time basis. Associate membership is available to others who lack the required years of experience but show promise of capability.

In addition to those who make consulting their sole profession, certain administrators with the permission of their boards accept occasional outside commitments. Others having reached retirement age are available for advice. More recently, management counselors and efficiency experts have joined the ranks. Such individuals or groups devote themselves to community surveys and hospital planning, as well as to studies of administrative or medical staff organization and professional services. The consultant supplements rather than duplicates the work of the architect. He formulates a plan from which the latter works. His fee is generally a fixed sum for conducting surveys or making administrative or medical audits. For projects involving hospital planning, construction, and equipment, he receives a percentage of the construction cost excluding land, architect's fees, and furnishings. Other financial settlements are reached through mutual agreement. It is desirable that both the consultant and the architect be brought into the proceedings in the early stages.

Lacking the services of a consultant, responsibility for the expansion program rests principally with the administrator and with the architect. Under such circumstances it is particularly desirable that the architect have some hospital background. Architects' fees are generally determined by the local chapter of the American Institute of Architects. The American Hospital Association supplies lists of qualified architects and consultants.

The trustee must necessarily depend on others for decisions in professional areas, but his business background is helpful in letting and signing contracts and in determining whether or not contracts should contain escalator clauses, be set up on a cost-plus basis, or on fixed fee.

Any plan involving expansion or new construction should include medical staff members, particularly chiefs of the various services. Their opinion is necessary in estimating changes to meet new demands in health care. Some allowance must be made for a natural tendency to push for their own specialties, as well as the possible fear of being absorbed by the hospital.

Professional assistance in future planning may be expected as well from the nursing director. Better than any one else she knows when the nursing stations are placed to insure adequate supervision over patient areas. She knows the extravagant waste of nurses' time in making long trips to and from utility rooms and she is aware of space limitations within which good nursing care can be safely provided.

The same principle pertains to the dietitian and other department heads. Floor arrangements that appear most logical and promising on paper, particularly in the eyes of the layman, can prove impractical in everyday use.

With an eye to the future, the presence of an active development program is essential for hospitals of all sizes. It supplements regional and area-wide planning. It rightfully assumes committee importance in the management pattern with representation from all facets of the hospital. In general terms it charts goals and evaluates resources working in conjunction with other planning groups.

Specifically it supplies the answers to such pertinent questions as: What type of hospital is it? What type of hospital should it be? How effective is its board of trustees and how competent its administrator? What services or specialties should it provide? If research is to be conducted, how will it be financed? To what extent does it engage in educating doctors, nurses, technicians, and others? Will it have full- or part-time physicians as chiefs of the major medical services? How much charity work will it do? How many out-patient clinics will it conduct?

The answers to these and similar questions should be checked with neighboring hospitals and health agencies to discover areas of duplication and areas that require expansion or curtailment depending upon population trends and community needs. Existing equipment and mechanical facilities need to be surveyed—the possibilities of coordination of certain functions being duly considered.

Provided with such a program the hospital will be prepared to justify its claims for public support. It then becomes the responsibility of the public to decide what standards of health care it would maintain and whether it will support the cost.

TELLING THE HOSPITAL STORY

EDUCATING THE PUBLIC to the importance of better health standards and disease prevention is an important responsibility of the community hospital. Trustees, administrators, and medical staff members must all be aware of the need to provide channels of communication with the community. Some specific devices for such education are: public lectures sponsored in conjunction with local health and school officials, printed matter distributed to visitors, and the use of radio, television, and films.

One small hospital located in a college town in Maine presents an outstanding example of effective public communication. To stimulate interest in good public health, and to point up the role played by the hospital, lectures on the fundamental concepts of physiology and hygiene are given at the hospital. Staff members explain the rudiments of anatomy, the functions of the clinical laboratory and the tests it performs. They describe how x-ray studies, deep therapy, and radioactive isotopes aid in the diagnosis and treatment of disease and how, through the tissue committee and medical audit, physicians evaluate their performance. They introduce the medical records room and explain the importance of its files. Officially known as the Society of Amateur Physicians and Surgeons, and sometimes informally referred to as SAPS, these knowledgeable citizens become ambassadors of good-will for the hospital in the community.

The same hospital offers lectures on weight reduction and posture for women. Courses in baby sitting for high school girls have focused attention upon careers in the health field and more specifically have aided nurse recruitment. The educational program likewise includes lectures for the clergy on the function of the hospital chaplain.

The average American, however, is unaware of the services he receives from his hospital. He has never had clearly explained to him the benefits made to his health care by the voluntary system, and why it is worth preserving. He is not aware of the concept of the hospital as the focal point of community health work.

What he does know and resents is the size of his hospital bill which under normal circumstances carries no explanation of cost. Sensational stories he reads in the local press pointing to neglect, professional errors, inefficient management confirm his suspicions. He fails to recognize that it is the unusual that makes news.

Hospital workers have been too busy practicing their professions to give much thought to the world outside. They have seen no need to publicize their services. They live and work within their institutions.

The need for a better informed public received its first impetus in 1932, when the American Hospital Association established its committee on education. This went directly to the core of the matter by listing the specific benefits to be gained from such procedure.

National Hospital Day, commemorating the birth of Florence Nightingale, was successful in encouraging visitors to inspect premises. Unfortunately, many such efforts ceased as hospital routine resumed its everyday course following the May 12th celebration.

The hospital story has never been adequately told. This sad fact has become increasingly apparent as the economic position of these institutions has grown acute. Initial efforts to encourage financial support on the part of business and industry revealed the embarrassing truth that there was no backlog of knowledge or understanding on which to present forceful appeals.

Today business representatives as well as the general public are developing understandable curiosity as to why hospitals in these days of labor-saving devices require two to two-and-a-half employees per patient to provide good care, what efforts are being taken to reduce that number, and why it costs $40,000 to add a single hospital room.

Public-relations programs too frequently resort to trick devices to catch the public's fleeting attention. They need to be formulated on broad basic policies reflecting the atmosphere of the institution, creating an accurate image of the team headed by the administrator and comprising trustees, doctors, researchers, nurses, professional and other employees, and auxiliary and volunteer members.

The tremendous changes taking place in community health patterns, with unmistakable threats to certain institutions, demand public interpretation. To win confidence for hospital management requires concerted effort.

Communications no longer can be established on a catch-as-catch-can basis. To be effective, basic knowledge of the subject involved must be acquired, as well as an awareness of the need to share that knowledge. Leadership must come from executive ranks with full support and counsel from the board of governors in cooperation with the medical staff. From such sources it will be channelled down the line to department heads and other employees. From such well oriented and knowledgeable hospital groups the story will percolate throughout the community.

As a community spokesman, the trustee needs to be able to talk convincingly before local and regional organizations and to make his voice heard effectively in legislative chambers. Despite his reluctance to fraternize with political figures or labor leaders he would do well to cultivate them and gain their support. To substantiate his arguments, he must have the latest facts and figures.

The medical staff member, too, may well function as a good-will ambassador. His word carries weight with his patients, and evidence of his loyalty to the hospital will prove convincing. Interpretation and clarification of hospital policies, factual explanation of the nursing shortage, and an understanding of the need to control over-utilization of hospital facilities will help counteract false impressions. To accomplish this successfully requires knowledge.

Similarly, nurses are in a position to describe to their patients the reasons for hospital procedures and policies, and conversely to transmit to their administrators their patients' needs. Hospital personnel, adequately oriented, can become important factors in influencing community opinion.

The joint conference committee offers excellent opportunities for promoting effective communication. Through closer contacts between doctors and lay members can come an accurate reflection of the community's attitudes which may serve as a guide to policies for the public-relations committee.

The public-relations committee, commonly a standing committee of the board, should include individuals with professional background—publishers, editors, journalists, or those involved with radio, television, and the graphic arts.

In the larger hospitals a public-relations director or counselor is essential. Such a person is particularly helpful in organizing and developing specific projects such as house organs, newspaper publicity, or annual reports. An alternative is to combine the director of public and personnel relations. The degree of organization depends upon the need, the size, and type of the hospital along with other local factors. Generally speaking, however, public relations is a full-time job.

The first step in any public-relations effort is to ascertain the community's attitude toward the hospital and the services it renders. This may already be apparent. If the sentiment is unfavorable, suspicion may be directed at the medical staff, the nursing department, the emergency room, or some other source. One spot that deserves special study is the admitting office. The most effective public-relations director cannot counteract the impressions made by an admitting officer who is indifferent and discourteous. Such first impressions are frequently lasting.

It has been recommended that the administrator, properly disguised, sit alongside his admitting desk and listen. Another productive listening post is adjacent to the telephone switchboard. If the executive is willing to learn the hard way, the next empty bed in his institution will prove a profitable educational experience.

Recognizing the need to develop new sources of financial support, many hospitals have created a position of director of development. This individual may also serve as public relations director, depending upon the size of the institution. Working closely with the board and administration he opens up channels of communication with individuals and groups whose financial support may prove substantial—foundation heads, business and industrial leaders, legislators, and attorneys. Under such a plan, one institution extended invitations to executives of neighboring industrial plants to have lunch at the hospital and to hear and see what was going on. Brief talks by members of the administrative and professional staffs explained procedures and costs. One item, in particular, created attention—the need to maintain hospital wage scales at the levels of those offered by industry for similar types of work.

Public appreciation and support have been gained by inviting carefully selected groups of citizens to have dinner at the hospital, followed by a tour of the institution. The board president, the administrator, and others describe various phases of the hospital's work with attention focused on costs. While not ostensibly a fund raising device, in many instances the financial returns have been gratifying.

Every hospital has a captive audience of patients who can do little more than listen or read. A good diversion for these patients would be to initiate them to hospital affairs during days of convalescence. Such contacts might take the form of printed material, explaining what is a modern voluntary hospital, how it is run, and the reasons for the rising costs of the services it renders. Early ambulation provides opportunities for visits to certain departments to learn firsthand what goes on. Motion pictures on health subjects will help define the place of the hospital in modern society.

Another effective medium to convey the hospital's story to the public is the auxiliary and volunteer groups. Too little has been done to recognize the value of these dedicated workers as interpreters of hospital service. Not only should they be adequately oriented, but they should be kept up to date on the functions of the modern hospital as a community health center.

It is a different hospital story we have to tell today—a story of recent advances and of future promises. It envisions broader perspectives of health care developed by each hospital in conjunction with local or regional hospital councils and associations.

The public is waiting to be told. It is asking questions, and while it waits for the answers it studies the health care package that the government may devise. The future of our voluntary system depends upon how convincing those answers are.

WANTED: LEADERSHIP

THE VOLUNTARY hospital system possesses great strengths. It also suffers certain weaknesses that must be corrected for it to survive increasing pressures. Tradition breeds inertia and the tendency is to remain complacent over past achievements.

Advances in medical science have far outdistanced the science of operational procedure. To fill in the gaps and accept new demands requires different attitudes and broader approaches by hospital heads.

Leadership is not to be confused with domination: the board president, for example, who clings persistently to his post year after year; the presiding officer who takes over at board meetings; the "steam roller" chairman, too quick with the gavel.

With due respect for the outstanding services rendered by many civic minded citizens, hospital policies are too often controlled by dominating individuals or cliques. Other members, not always well informed on health affairs serve as standbys, ready to give passive acceptance to rulings predicated more often on past performances than on future needs.

Today, hospitals have become the public's business, about which it entertains considerable concern. This requires wider representation in public health affairs on the part of policy makers with broader perspectives and philosophies of medical care. The same management methods that have been used successfully by industry in merchandising might well be applied to public health.

True hospital leadership guides or shows the way, forging a chain of professional units into a strong health front. It starts at the top level with the hospital president or board chairman. His effectiveness as policy maker and public representative is influenced by the quality of support he receives from his executive officer and his willingness to accept the counsel of others who are professionally trained. Opportunities to exert his influence lie in two directions—within the hospital organization and outside in surrounding areas. One logical beginning may lie in an appraisal of board functions.

Casting tradition aside, the hospital leader, in conjunction with his administrator, may justifiably reappraise the composition of the board, its members, its committees, and its objectives. In doing so, he may borrow from his business background, always recognizing the basic differences between the two. He will satisfy himself that the hospital is performing its proper social functions effectively, assuring its survival under voluntary auspices.

As leader he may well recognize the fallacy of trying to get results from an oversized and underoriented trustee group. Frequently he will find himself asking "why change?" Having gained new insight into the complexities of the situation his original question may shift to "why not?"

Why not reconstruct the pattern of the governing board? Its potentials may be realized more successfully by the three-way approach previously described—junior or associate, active, and honorary. Taking a lead from industry, the hospital head may envision a board combining community representation with certain staff specialists. Under such circumstances, membership may include six or eight laymen, the administrator, medical director, a physician representing the medical board, the controller, and the nursing director.

Such a management pattern is still in the discussion stage—from which it may never emerge. A more conservative approach would be to expand membership in the joint conference committee to include nursing and other department heads.

Leadership is particularly essential in promoting mutually satisfactory relationships between hospitals and their medical staffs. Despite the trustee's responsibility for the cost and the quality of medical and nursing services, he is frequently unable to take action because of lack of information. As a layman, he requires the support of sound professional counsel. This is all the more reason for exercising care in making staff appointments.

The medical staff has justifiable cause for questioning the authority of the board and the administrator. Chief among these are their lack of medical background and their reluctance to accept the doctor as a partner in the total operation of the hospital.

The hospital official whose interests have been centered upon one institution should deliberately establish contact with those serving in similar capacities within the surrounding community. Under his leadership, plans will develop assuring better over-all health coverage at costs held within reasonable limits. Involvements in such outside activities as regional and state planning agencies and Blue Cross negotiations will also prove helpful. His influence should be felt in political circles, with the hope of gaining financial recognition from local government for services rendered to indigent patients. Contacts with the heads of labor unions may help to forestall employee conflict. He should accept assignments to participate in regional studies and surveys for which his knowledge and training may fit him.

Nowhere can insight into hospital problems better be gained than in participating in the work of state hospital associations. Among other advantages this contributes to closer cooperation between lay and professional interests. Certain trustees have assumed the offices of president or vice-president of such groups.

Preparation for hospital leadership can be formally accomplished through carefully planned orientation sessions or informally through effective communication between the new head and the administrator and medical staff members.

In addition to the educational opportunities offered within the hospital under the tutelage of the administrator and others, numerous institutes and workshops sponsored by hospital associations and universities are available to those who would extend their knowledge. On such occasions opportunities are provided to hear authorities analyze critical issues affecting modern health care, including the threat of government domination and the potential effect of Medicare upon hospital facilities. Discussion and an interchange of thought will focus the spotlight on issues that face us.

Competent leadership demands continuous study. In this respect the hospital board member is no different than the doctor or other specialist. His education is never finished.

National Agencies and Standards

THE AMERICAN HOSPITAL ASSOCIATION

THE FIRST STEP toward a national organization for improved administration of hospitals was taken in 1898 with the founding of the Association of Hospital Superintendents. In 1906 this group became the American Hospital Association. Today, with headquarters in Chicago, and branch offices in New York City, Washington, and San Francisco, the organization speaks and acts for a broad range of hospital and health agencies.

Institutional membership in the American Hospital Association includes short- and long-term hospitals in the United States and other countries, also dispensaries and clinics, Blue Cross plans, hospital auxiliaries, and allied health agencies. These along with individual memberships bring the total enrollment to over 12,000. Although control of the Association's affairs rests with administrators, increasing numbers of trustees participate in its various activities.

Institutional, associate, and personal memberships are provided in the Association's bylaws. These are available to institutions or individuals interested in the Association's objectives. Hospital membership dues are allocated according to the type of institution and the service it renders. General and special hospitals rendering services primarily to patients with conditions normally requiring short-stay pay on the basis of days of patient-service rendered, newborn infant days excluded. Associate members, organizations interested in the Association not eligible for institutional membership, pay from $90 to $180. Dues for individuals associated with institutional members are $15, with the exception of full-time students in hospital administration, who are enrolled for $7.50.

The American Hospital Association, according to its bylaws, serves the following purposes: to promote the welfare of the people through the development of hospital and out-patient service; to encourage professional education and scientific research; to aid in the health education of the public; to co-operate with other organizations having similar objectives; to distribute factual knowledge with regard to the various specialized services and functions of hospitals; to coordinate such knowledge into an integrated pattern of activity for pursuance by all hospitals; to coordinate the plans, problems, actions, and needs of all hospitals for the benefit of individual members.

To provide continuity to the Association's affairs, each new president, a hospital administrator, serves for three years: first as president-elect, then as president and finally as immediate past-president. These three officers with twelve trustees, including two Blue Cross representatives, constitute the board of trustees. Trustees serve three-year terms.

The Association's direction is centered in a House of Delegates composed of 127 members. One hundred are chosen by members of each state, the District of Columbia, Puerto Rico, and Canada. Twelve delegates at large are elected at each annual meeting by the House. In addition the officers and trustees, also elected by the delegates, sit in the House.

On recommendation of the president, the trustees appoint members to the Association's nine councils. These are: Council on Administration, Council on Association Services, Council on Blue Cross and Finance, Council on Government Relations,

Council on Hospital Auxiliaries, Council on Professional Practice, Council on Long-Term Care, Council on Nursing and Council on Research and Planning. The board also appoints the executive vice-president, secretary, treasurer, assistant treasurer, and assistant secretary. Chairmen of the councils plus the president, comprise a General Council which meets five times a year to review existing programs and recommend new ones. Originally, individual members volunteered their time and abilities to various phases of the work. Now, due to larger assessments, councils are headed by paid specialists.

Among other contributions, the Association has helped hospitals preserve their tax exempt status, encouraged social security benefits for employees, and endorsed acceptance of prepaid hospital and medical insurance plans, notably Blue Cross and Blue Shield. It has been instrumental in the development of the Hill-Burton Act, which provides federal grants to states to pay part of the cost of constructing governmental and voluntary, nonprofit hospitals, and related health agencies. Originally these funds were allocated exclusively to new hospital construction, but more recently they have been extended to include the modernization of existing facilities. National surveys of hospital care, financing health care for the aged, and problems of long-term illness have been conducted under the Association's sponsorship.

A hospital listing program is conducted annually by the Association. This provides a national census of some 7,000 hospitals, and a variety of significant statistics on physical plants, utilization, finances, personnel, and services. Inclusion in this group is among the requirements for accreditation by the Joint Commission on Accreditation of Hospitals.

To answer frequent requests for advice on new hospital construction, the Association offers a roster of architects who meet certain criteria, and a list of fund raising councils and consultants whose competence and fair practice have been demonstrated. Application must be made for approval. The Associaton similarly has established approval standards for nonprofit hospital service plans.

Regional workshops, institutes, short courses, and invitational conferences, covering subjects that range from accounting to x-ray, play an important part in the Association's educational program. Most important among its meetings is its annual four-day convention which attracts over 10,000 persons engaged in professional health care—administrators, doctors, surgeons, trustees, auxiliary members, and volunteers.

Three publications are issued by the Association. "Hospitals," published twice-monthly, is addressed to administrators. "Trustee," a monthly pocket-size magazine is directed to board members, and "The Auxiliary Leader" reaches some 7,000 volunteer workers. In addition, the Association distributes among its members five monthly news letters, manuals and monographs, many of which are translated into Spanish or French.

The Asa S. Bacon Memorial Library containing over 20,000 volumes on hospitals, hospital administration, and other health activities is located in the Association's headquarters in Chicago. These provide source material for members in the form of bibliographies and the loan of books, pamphlets, and other printed matter. Films on various phases of hospital service also are available.

The Association's Washington Service Bureau under the direction of a full-time chief, keeps the membership informed on federal government activities that are of vital interest to hospital administrators, and represents the community hospital's viewpoint on the federal level. This Bureau serves also as the Pan-American office of the International Hospital Federation, representing the hospitals of the western hemisphere.

STATE AND OTHER GROUPS

SUPPLEMENTING THE SERVICES of the American Hospital Association are regional, state, and metropolitan hospital bodies. Some twelve regional associations now hold annual meetings and exhibits. They also conduct studies and surveys in specific areas of health work and other administrative operations. Outstanding examples are the New England Hospital Assembly, which meets each year in Boston, and the Tri-State Assembly, which annually attracts thousands of hospital people to Chicago.

State associations serve their memberships, frequently under the direction of full-time secretaries, in meeting such district problems as legislation, State representation, education, and public relations. These groups, too, hold annual meetings. Financing is provided, primarily, through institutional membership dues and personal membership and exhibitor rentals at annual conventions. Administrators of member institutions serve commonly as trustees.

More local in scope are the functions of metropolitan hospital groups or councils. These concentrate on labor relations, group purchasing, public relations, and community planning. They operate with boards of directors, including hospital trustees, and other persons interested in public health and civic affairs. Depending upon their size and scope, a full-time executive is in charge.

Because the majority of voluntary hospitals have religious affiliation, it is logical they should have their own sponsoring bodies. Of these the largest is the Catholic Hospital Association, founded in 1915, with headquarters in Saint Louis, Missouri. Concerned chiefly with the religious aspects of Catholic hospitals, it conducts educational programs and publishes "Hospital Progress," a monthly journal for administrators and department heads. Its annual convention attracts large attendance and includes a substantial number of exhibits.

The Protestant group likewise has its own association—The American Protestant Hospital Association, founded in 1921. Each year it holds an annual convention. Because Methodist institutions dominate in the Protestant field, that church sponsors a separate organization known as the Board of Hospitals and Homes.

Of more recent origin is the International Hospital Federation, whose members include hospital associations, groups, and individuals representing some 60 nations. The purpose is to stimulate an international exchange of information on hospital affairs. From a somewhat unauspicious beginning, the Federation is assuming new importance, with a full-time director general operating from headquarters in London. Plans are under way for a quarterly publication and programs for seminars to be held in various countries.

THE JOINT COMMISSION ON ACCREDITATION OF HOSPITALS

ACCREDITATION GIVES to a hospital the same recognition of quality as the stamp of "sterling" on silver. It provides assurance that certain standards in patient care formulated by physicians are being met and that doctors and hospital heads are working together on behalf of the community's health interests. Accreditation is granted today by the Commission upon the request of a hospital.

This effort to assure the public that its health care is in competent hands may be traced to the founding of the American Medical Association in 1847, and particularly to the founding of the Association's Council on Medical Education and Hospitals in 1905. The Council approves hospitals for intern training and for residencies and fellowships in specialties, as well as for educating x-ray technicians, medical-records librarians, occupational and physical therapists, and medical technologists.

The American College of Surgeons, founded in 1913, inaugurated in 1918 a program of minimal standards. These standards included a well organized, complete, and ethical medical staff conducting regular conferences for review of the clinical work, accurate and complete records of all patients treated, and adequate facilities for diagnostic and therapeutic procedures, including a clinical laboratory and x-ray department. Fee splitting in any form was considered a violation of medical ethics. Other requisites were properly conceived and executed bylaws and rules and regulations, competent administration, suitable provisions for education and research, and a physical plant meeting every requirement for nutrition, cleanliness, and good hospital practice.

When, in 1950, it was rumored that the American College of Surgeons was giving up its standardization program, considerable conjecture developed over what group would take over. After some debate, the Joint Commission on Accreditation of Hospitals was established in 1952, as an independent, voluntary nonprofit organization whose primary objective is the improvement of patient care. Under its auspices, accreditation is granted based on standards formulated by physicians in the best interests of patient care, following voluntary inspections.

The Joint Commission is now sponsored by the American Hospital Association, the American College of Surgeons, the American Medical Association, and the American College of Physicians. A board of twenty commissioners, seven each from the American Medical Association and the American Hospital Association, and three each from the American College of Physicians and the American College of Surgeons are elected by the board on nomination by the sponsoring agencies. These commissioners develop and publish standards and act upon the reports of trained medical staff members, following personal surveys.

Under such auspices, the minimal standard program initiated by the American College of Surgeons is maintained with added emphasis on laboratory examinations of all tissues removed from patients, authoritative committees of the medical staff to review findings, appraise quality, and take action when necessary, and regular clinical meetings of the medical staff for the review of cases.

The standards on which the surveyor bases his judgment are listed in "Standards for Hospital Accreditation," published by the Joint Commission. Such facilities and services must be maintained as dietary, medical records, pharmacy or drug room, clinical pathology and pathological anatomy, radiology, and emergency care for mass casualties. Similarly the surveyor evaluates the governing board, administration, and medical staff. Based on the report rendered, the twenty members of the Joint Commission may grant accreditation for three years, or for one year, or withhold it. A hospital may not maintain the one-year status indefinitely. After two consecutive surveys resulting in accreditation for one year, the hospital must, on the third survey, achieve accreditation for three years, or be reduced to nonaccreditation.

Full professional accreditation provides assurance to trustees, administration, personnel, patients, and the public that the institution has attained and is maintaining certain minimal standards. Restricted accreditation or withdrawal of accreditation therefore indicates need for prompt and decisive action.

Absence of accreditation in rare instances may be attributed to limitations in size and resources, rather than to poor standards, and does not necessarily reflect on care rendered. According to recent figures, about 60 percent of all general hospitals are accredited. The proportion drops as the size of the institution grows smaller. It is these that have greatest need for help. Certain Blue Cross plans will not pay participating hospital's fees to those that remain unaccredited.

Every hospital of 25 beds or more can apply for accreditation if it has been in operation for at least twelve months and is listed by the American Hospital Association.

Smaller institutions occasionally complain that because of their size, they should not be penalized for failing to adhere to the same standards as bigger institutions. The standards established are minimal and no hospital should be rendering service that cannot meet them.

UPGRADING EXECUTIVE MANAGEMENT

ALONG WITH UPGRADING of the standards of hospital services, the need to raise the level of executive management became obvious. This resulted in the formation in 1933 of the American College of Hospital Administrators to provide educational opportunities for hospital administrators and to obtain recognition for those serving competently in this area.

Specifically the aims of the College are: to elevate the standards of hospital administration; to develop and promote standards of education, training, and competence for hospital administrators; to educate hospital trustees and the public that the practice of hospital administration calls for special training and experience; and to provide a method for conferring fellowships on those who have done or are doing noteworthy service in the field of hospital administration.

The College is nonpolitical, nonsectarian and is open to administrators and assistant administrators, based on experience, training and the successful completion of written and oral examinations. Once accepted as a nominee, the individual progresses to the rank of member and fellow. Membership in the College now numbers over 6,000.

The organization pattern of the College constitutes a board

of eight governors, one from each of seven districts in the United States and one from Canada. In addition a Council of Regents of 53 members represents the states and provinces. The president is a hospital administrator working wth an executive vice-president who is a full-time, salaried official appointed by the board of governors.

Under such auspices basic and advanced institutes and seminars are held for those actively engaged in hospital administration as well as for those entering the profession. The College's yearly "Congress," a three-day management conference, attracts administrators from all sections of the country. A quarterly journal, "Hospital Administration," and a monthly newsletter are also among its services.

Suggested Reading

BOOKS

BAUMGARTEN, HAROLD, JR. *Concepts of Nursing Home Administration: A Manual for Executives of Prolonged Illness Institutions*. New York: The Macmillan Company, 1965.

CUNNINGHAM, ROBERT M., JR. *Hospitals, Doctors and Dollars*. New York: F. W. Dodge Corp, 1961.

GEORGOPOULOS, BASIL S., MANN, FLOYD C. *The Community General Hospital*. New York: The Macmillan Company, 1962.

GREENBERG, SELIG. *The Troubled Calling, Crisis in the Medical Establishment*. New York: The Macmillan Company, 1965.

KLARMAN, HERBERT E. *Hospital Care in New York City*. New York: Columbia University Press, 1963.

KNOWLES, JOHN H., M.D. *Hospitals, Doctors and the Public Interest*. Cambridge, Mass.: Harvard University Press, 1965.

LETOURNEAU, CHARLES U., M.D. *Hospital Trusteeship*. Chicago: Starling Publications, 1959.

MCGIBONY, JOHN R., M.D. *Handbook for Hospital Trustees*. College Park, Md.: Hospital Publications, Inc., 1965.

MILLS, ALDEN B. *Hospital Public Relations Today*. Berwyn, Ill.: Physicians' Record Co., 1965.

OWEN, JOSEPH K. *Modern Concepts of Hospital Administration*. Philadelphia: W. B. Saunders Co., 1962.

SOMERS, HERMAN M., SOMERS, ANNE R. *Doctors, Patients and Health Insurance*. Washington, D. C.: The Brookings Institution, 1961.

JOURNALS AND PERIODICALS

The Auxiliary Leader. American Hospital Association, 840 North Lake Shore Drive, Chicago, Ill. Published monthly.

Hospital Management. Clissold Publishing Company, 105 West Adams Street, Chicago, Ill. Published monthly.

Hospital Progress. Official Journal of the Catholic Hospital Association, 1438 South Grand Boulevard, St. Louis, Mo. Published monthly.

Hospitals. Journal of the American Hospital Association, 840 North Lake Shore Drive, Chicago, Ill. Published monthly.

The Modern Hospital. McGraw Hill Publications, 1050 Merchandise Mart, Chicago, Ill. Published monthly.

Trustee. Journal for Hospital Governing Boards. American Hospital Association, 840 North Lake Shore Drive, Chicago, Ill. Published monthly.

Index